The Open University

Technology: Level 2
T211 Workbook 1

Workbook 1

Modelling Workbook

Prepared on behalf of the Course Team by Steve Garner

T211 DESIGN AND DESIGNING

This publication forms part of an Open University course T211. Details of this and other Open University courses can be obtained from the Course Information and Advice Centre, PO Box 724, The Open University, Milton Keynes MK7 6ZS, United Kingdom: tel. +44 (0)1908 653231, e-mail ces-gen@open.ac.uk

Alternatively, you may visit the Open University website at http://www.open.ac.uk where you can learn more about the wide range of courses and packs offered at all levels by The Open University.

To purchase this publication or other components of Open University courses, contact Open University Worldwide Ltd, The Open University, Walton Hall, Milton Keynes MK7 6AA, United Kingdom: tel. +44 (0)1908 858785;
fax +44 (0)1908 858787; e-mail ouwenq@open.ac.uk;
website http://www.ouw.co.uk

The Open University
Walton Hall, Milton Keynes
MK7 6AA

First published 2004. Second edition 2006.

Edited, designed and typeset by The Open University.

Printed and bound in the United Kingdom by The Alden Group, Oxford.

ISBN0 7492 0496 6

2.1

Contents

Activities

Toolkit

The activities in this workbook introduce you to particular pieces of drawing and modelling equipment. To assist you in assembling your own modelling toolkit this list identifies what you will need and when you will need it. Drawing equipment and media are available in various qualities and at various prices and in general I advise you to purchase the *inexpensive* ranges. Some papers are provided in the T211 *Paper pack* and other items, for example newspapers and scrap paper, should be easy to find.

Activity 1	Basic ball-point pen, newspaper.
Activity 2	Three pencils (soft 3B–6B, medium HB-B and hard 2H–4H) plus a few sheets of scrap plain paper (A4).
Activity 3	Thin cardboard (a large empty cereal packet is fine), any pencil, ruler (showing millimetres), scissors, adhesive tape (e.g. masking tape). If needed, a photocopy of chair components and paper and card glue.
Activity 4	Thin cardboard (as above), any pencil, ruler (showing millimetres), scissors, paper and card glue or adhesive tape, a few coloured pens or pencils (optional).
Activity 5	Thin card (as above), some scrap plain paper (A4), scissors, ruler, any pencil, paper and card glue or adhesive tape, a few coloured pens or pencils.
Activity 6	Thin card (as above), scissors, ruler, any pen or pencil, adhesive tape or glue.
Activity 7	Pencil (HB, B or 2B), A4 sheet of squared paper from the *Paper pack*, the card model from Activity 3, ruler, eraser.
Activity 8	An inexpensive fine-point ink or ball-point pen, two sheets of tracing paper or layout paper (from the *Paper pack*).
Activity 9	Ball-point or fine-point pen, two A4 sheets of squared paper (from the *Paper pack*), ruler.
Activity 10	Any pencil, A4 sheet of plain paper, eraser.
Activity 11	B or 2B pencil, eraser, ruler, A3 sheet of plain paper.
Activity 12	B or 2B pencil, eraser, ruler, A3 sheet of plain paper.
Activity 13	B or 2B pencil, eraser, A4 sheet of plain paper. If needed: tracing or layout paper.
Activity 14	B or 2B pencil, eraser, ruler, two A4 sheets of plain paper.
Activity 15	Ball-point or fine-point pen, drawings (or photocopies) from Activity 14, A4 sheet of layout paper.
Activity 16	B or 2B pencil, eraser, ruler, A4 sheet of plain paper, large sheet of scrap paper.
Activity 17	B or 2B pencil, eraser, ruler, A3 sheet of plain paper.
Activity 18	B or 2B pencil or any pen, eraser, ruler, A3 sheet of plain and A4 sheet of tracing paper, scrap paper.

Activity 19	B or 2B pencil or any pen, eraser, A4 sheet of plain paper, a few sheets of scrap plain paper.
Activity 20	B or 2B pencil or any pen, eraser, A4 sheets of plain paper, tracing paper, and squared paper.

Introduction

This Modelling Workbook has been produced to help you develop:

- *skills and abilities*, for example sketching, to exploit in creating and communicating your own designing activity;
- *knowledge* of why designers make models, what types of models are relevant in designing, and when each might be used.

This workbook also functions as a manual of techniques, materials and tools allowing you to select and collect resources for designing. It includes an introduction to modern design modelling techniques such as computer-based modelling. Flick through the whole workbook. You'll see that that it is heavily illustrated and in many cases you will be guided, step-by-step, through techniques for drawing and model making. It is intended that this workbook supports all six blocks in T211 and the links will be made clear as you progress through the material. It also has links to the course DVD so that you can use audio-visual resources to help you develop your skills and knowledge of design modelling.

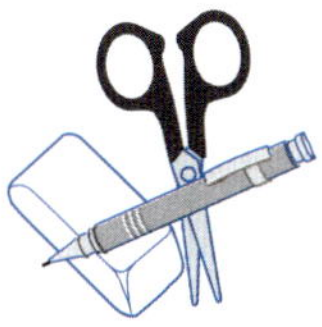

Whenever you see the equipment icon various tools, equipment or media are being discussed and recommended for purchase. In this way you can build up your own modelling toolkit – a collection of basic tools and media to assist your own designing. The items you need for each activity are listed at the front of the workbook.

Blocks 1–5 refer you to specific sections or activities in the workbook. They will have a specific purpose at that point in the course, for example, they might develop skills and knowledge relevant to the tutor-marked assignment (TMA) for that block or illustrate, via your activity, particular points made in a block. In this way the workbook supports some of the key learning outcomes of the course.

Being able to draw images and to build physical models is central to the activity of designing. Drawing and making assist us to 'think in three dimensions' but such skill can only come about through practice. If you get into the habit of carrying a notebook and thinking with sketches then your designing will be enhanced. I hope that you'll also develop the confidence to explore design ideas by making quick, rough models, for example in cardboard. If you develop skills with the techniques presented here you will improve your ability to communicate, to share ideas, to specify your intentions, to instruct others clearly and to test ideas. Perhaps most importantly, these modelling techniques can enable you to externalise your own thoughts – to give shape to new ideas – and as such they can provide vital support to creative design thinking.

I hope that you will return often to this workbook. It seeks to support the absolute beginner and those more accomplished in design modelling. It has been designed so that it forms a useful modelling resource even after you have completed the course.

Section 1 opens with an essay on models and modelling in design by Dr Mark Evans, an industrial designer. Read through this first to get an overview but you may want to revisit it later to read it in more detail once you have undertaken some of the activities.

1

Modelling strategies and product design

Mark Evans

This essay discusses a range of modelling techniques available to product designers today. It illustrates the co-existence of conventional (non-computer) and digital techniques. Illustrations from the author's own professional practice are included and these chart the progression of a number of projects from first concepts to pre-production appearance prototypes.

Successful design demands that we use the most appropriate modelling strategy for each stage of the designing process – from the earliest idea to the finished product. We need to use the right model at the right time. Each modelling type, whether it be freehand sketching, rough modelling in cardboard or computer-based modelling has its own qualities which make it more or less suitable at any given stage of the design process. To do otherwise can lead to significant reductions in effectiveness, weaker communication with colleagues, wasted investment in resources and longer development time.

Whether individual designers or design teams employ two-dimensional (2D), three-dimensional (3D) or virtual (computer generated) modelling techniques, the key requirement is for the modelling method to be appropriate to the required outcome. For example, the need to support the free flow of ideas at the beginning of product design activity necessitates modelling techniques that facilitate rapid and creative ideas generation. The economy of simple pen or pencil sketching means it is still widely employed at the conceptual design stage. Producing sketches requires some skill and knowledge but the time required to make the drawing, and the costs of the resources, is minimal. Sketching allows designers to visualise ideas. The images provide a means of examining our ideas – or of sharing them with others and they can contain a significant level of complex detail if necessary. The economy of sketching means that designers can easily change direction in their thinking. This is vital to creativity because good ideas might require a redefining of a problem as well as the generation of possible solutions. Models that were costly or time-consuming to make at this stage might inhibit our willingness to change direction.

At the other end of the spectrum are closely defined and specified models such as test rigs or models, which although they don't work, are superficially identical to the intended product. These models can take weeks to build. It is usually only worth going to this expense if the design problem is well understood and the proposal seems to offer a manufacturable and marketable solution.

Over recent years, the range of modelling techniques available to the product designer has increased significantly, with new computer-based modelling systems making a major contribution. With a wide range of digital design tools available, product designers must select not only which new technologies to employ, but identify how these might be integrated with traditional modelling techniques and tools.

1.1 Concept sketches

Drawing is a key skill for the product designer. Speed and spontaneity are essential features of concept sketching as the designer moves relatively quickly from one idea to the next. Concept sketches are usually line drawings. The choice of media is personal, but pencil, biro and fine-line pens are favoured by designers. Concept sketching can be used in many ways from exploring ideas to conveying complex three-dimensional (3D) form and technical detail. An example of concept sketching undertaken during the design of a lawnmower can be seen in Figure 1. Some images present a rough estimation of perspective drawing to give an overall 'picture' of the product while other images show only a side or plan view. You can see that some ideas have been 'worked up' while others remain vague and undeveloped. The sketches reveal the designer 'thinking with their pen'. In this example no colour has been added, perhaps because at this stage the designer was thinking about how the product would work. However, it's quite common to find colour added to some sketches so that they stand out. For example, colour might be vital to the concept design of fashion clothing or food packaging.

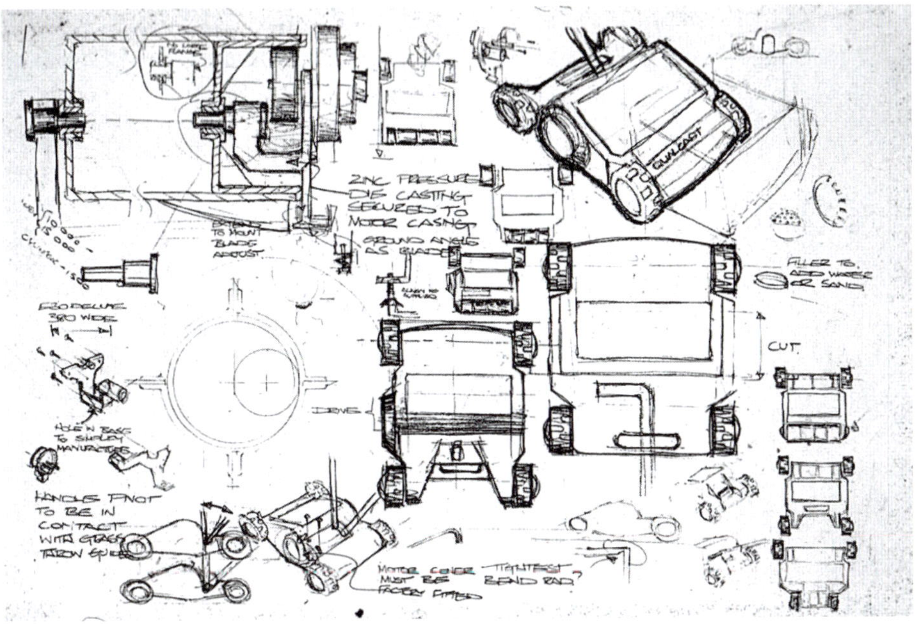

Figure 1 Concept sketches made as a designer works out initial ideas for a new model of a lawnmower

1.2 Sketch renderings

Sketch rendering is a more sophisticated form of concept sketching and involves the application of colour, tone and detail to add realism. Sketch renderings work by adding to or clarifying information in a basic sketch. The key to effective sketch rendering is the use of colour with speed and spontaneity. It is common to find sketch renderings used alongside concept sketches but they can also be used to illustrate proposals for design meetings.

An example of sketch renderings produced during the design of children's cutlery can be seen in Figure 2. Since the product is a relatively simple one it doesn't need to be shown in perspective. Colour and tone have been added to basic elevation drawings to provide a stronger illusion of three-dimensions.

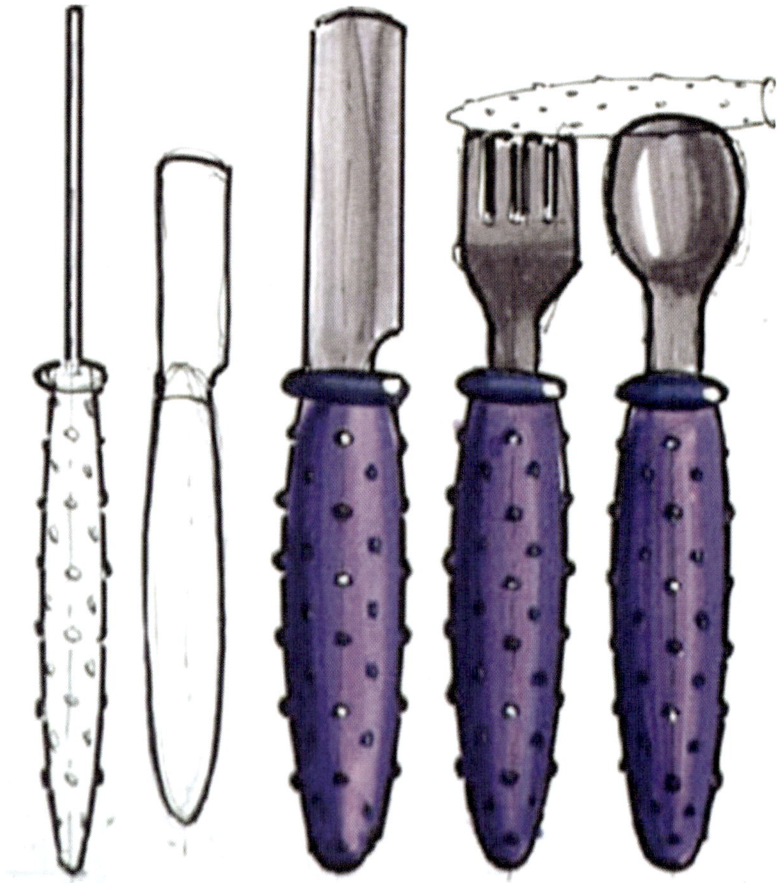

Figure 2 Sketch rendering made during the design of children's cutlery

1.3 Conventional renderings

A formal presentation of design ideas to clients usually requires highly realistic drawings so that clients can interpret and evaluate the design proposal. A more controlled form of rendering is generally used here. Conventional renderings may include a variety of colour media such as watercolour, drawing inks, gouache, acrylics, oil paint, pastel, pencil crayon and airbrush, but the professional marker pen has evolved as the preferred option because of its convenience, quick drying time and range of colours.

An example of a rendered side view of a lawnmower produced by using ink, marker and crayon can be seen in Figure 3. One of the reasons why this side view successfully conveys three-dimensional form is the consistent rendering of highlights and shadow. A white crayon has been used to lighten the upper surfaces of the lawnmower casing and the wheel treads as if light were falling on them. The underside of the central casing is deeply shaded. Look at the yellow handle at the rear and particularly at the circular form within the handle. How do you read this circular form, is it concave or convex? You should see it as concave – as an indentation – because the shading has been placed at the top of the circle and the highlight at the base (assuming the source of the light is overhead).

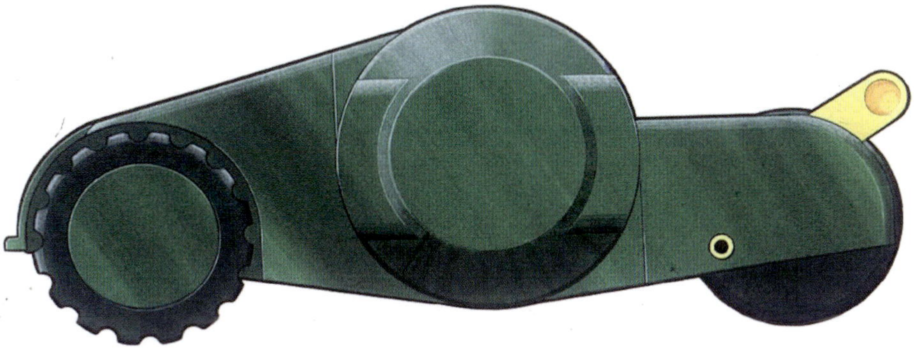

Figure 3 Mixed media rendering produced during the design of a lawnmower

1.4 3D rough models

Designers often construct simple physical models of their product ideas early in the design process so that they can handle and evaluate them. These are 3D rough models. They can be produced relatively quickly from basic information drawn on paper. Sometimes they are produced before, or in parallel with, concept sketching. A wide range of materials can be used, but card and rigid cellular foam are popular. Shapes and details can be defined during the making process and therefore rough modelling can be very useful in the generation and exploration of design ideas. The aim of rough modelling is to define the basic proportions, surfaces and form.

An example of a rough model for the handle of a nylon-line grass trimmer produced in styrofoam can be seen in Figure 4. Styrofoam is a very lightweight, rigid cellular foam that can be cut easily with knives or a handsaw. It's purchased in large blocks and cut up to suit each job. Creating fine detail is relatively easy since it can be drilled, filed and even carved with a sheet of sandpaper. Of course the feedback one obtains from such 3D models is limited. They don't represent the weight of the intended product and the surface quality is completely different. However, they can be useful for getting quick feedback regarding human interaction or for judging visual qualities such as proportion.

Figure 4 Rough model produced during the industrial design of a nylon-line grass trimmer

Despite the extensive use of computer modelling techniques, industrial designers continue to maintain their enthusiasm for 3D rough models, perhaps because such constructions can be held in the hand, evaluated and shared.

1.5 Principle-proving models

In contrast to 3D rough models, principle-proving models seek to examine technical performance. Again, speed and spontaneity are key qualities, with simple fabrication techniques being used to ascertain the viability of the concept. Such models may display components that look nothing like the eventual parts and the overall form may be bulky and ugly but the model can assist the designer or design team to identify basic principles for further development – and reject early those that are unlikely to work. An example of a principle-proving model of a new drive system, produced during the concept generation of the lawnmower, can be seen in Figure 5. A variety of found materials may be incorporated in such a model.

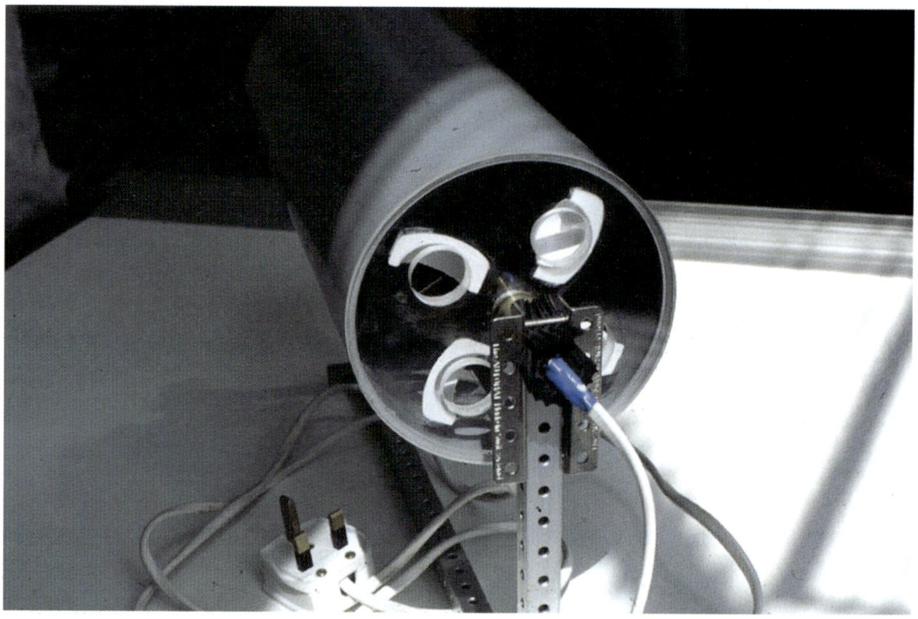

Figure 5 Principle-proving model of a drive system produced during the industrial design of a lawnmower

1.6 Working models and prototypes

As a design progresses, and as further details and components are added, so the accuracy of the modelling must increase. At this stage the design team will be involved in various types of design work. For example, in the lawnmower project, part of the team was concerned with the production of a technical proposal capable of meeting the design specification while other members of the team were concerned with the outer form – making it easy and safe to use as well as attractive. Each group produced very different types of working model. Some models closely resembled aspects of the intended lawnmower such as the motor and drive system. These detailed and working models are more correctly called 'prototypes'.

During the design of the grass trimmer, a fully working prototype was produced to evaluate cutting performance using a range of batteries and motors. Whilst this did not look like the production item, it had the major advantage of providing a relatively accurate representation of weight and balance that could be used to generate feedback from people selected as potential users (see Figure 6).

Figure 6 Prototype nylon-line grass trimmer being tested

1.7 3D Computer Aided Design (CAD)

The timing for the introduction of computer-based modelling will vary from project to project, and it reflects the working practices of particular designers. Until recently, most CAD systems required significant skill and time on the part of the operator in order to create even the most basic 3D model on the computer. The procedures were deemed too slow to suit the rapid turnover of ideas in concept design and CAD was usually only brought in when a concept had been defined. The situation is changing with easier-to-use CAD systems and it is now suitable for even the earliest stages of design where speed and spontaneity are important. However, many companies still only invest in the production of CAD models once the basic design concept has been defined.

The production of front, side and plan views via a two-dimensional (2D) CAD programme is relatively straightforward but the models are basic. They are the equivalent of the paper-based 'blueprints' that used to supply the detailed technical information necessary for manufacturing a product or component. 3D CAD can provide an efficient means of representing complex component geometry, enabling the designer to not only accurately define and manipulate 3D form but export this geometry to other computer based tools such as those for visualisation and rapid prototyping.

Once a proposal has been drawn in a 3D CAD system the designer can use its rendering capabilities, or other rendering software, to produce realistic visualisations. Unlike those generated using manual techniques, CAD renderings are an exact representation of the proposal as the visualisations are translated directly from the 3D geometry. Examples of CAD renderings produced during the design of the range of children's cutlery can be seen in Figures 7 and 8.

Figure 7 CAD rendering of children's cutlery

Unlike with manual techniques, changes can be made to the viewing angle or colours of the proposal by redefining parameters. For example, by rearranging the 3D geometry and specifying different material properties and finishes, a range of colour options for the cutlery was produced in a fraction of the time compared with using manual techniques (see Figure 8).

Once approved, the 3D geometry employed in CAD can be used for engineering evaluations such as finite element analysis, component clash detection and mould-flow analysis, along with computer numeric control (CNC) machining of prototype and production tooling.

Figure 8 CAD rendering of colour options for children's cutlery

1.8 Rapid prototyping

As the geometry produced on the CAD system is an accurate description of form, it is possible to translate this into physical objects through the use of rapid prototyping. Rapid prototyping involves the production of components from 3D CAD geometry using various build techniques. In contrast to 2D CAD or manual drawing board techniques, the designer does not have to produce discreet component drawings to enable the build to take place as the 3D geometry is directly translated into the physical components.

Whilst rapid prototyping was originally devised for the production of relatively robust components for engineering evaluation, faster and lower cost systems have emerged that find applications in many fields. New techniques that work by hardening layers of starch or building up layers of wax are now being used to create visually accurate product components. Known as concept modellers, these rapid prototyping systems can be particularly useful during the early phases of product design in a similar way to the rigid foam sketch models previously discussed. Figure 9 shows a range of sizes of handles produced for the children's cutlery using a powder-based process of building the parts up in layers.

Figure 9 Rapid prototype models of handles for children's cutlery
Note the stepped surface on the centre and left models.

Whilst suitable for basic evaluation, for a more accurate definition of the product form it is necessary to remove the 'stepping' on the surfaces that occurs as a result of the layer-based build process. If you look closely at the centre and left handles shown in Figure 9 you'll see the fine steps which look a bit like the grain of wood. This stepping usually necessitates hand finishing to smooth the surfaces. Components can then be painted and assembled to produce products that can closely resemble production items.

More robust components can be produced using other rapid prototyping techniques such as stereolithography, fused deposition modelling and selective laser sintering. Stereolithography involves the hardening of a photo-sensitive epoxy resin using an ultra violet laser and results in a component with a translucent amber-coloured finish. These are more suitable for engineering and ergonomic evaluation.

An example of the use of stereolithography to produce a battery compartment for the nylon-line trimmer can be seen in Figure 10.

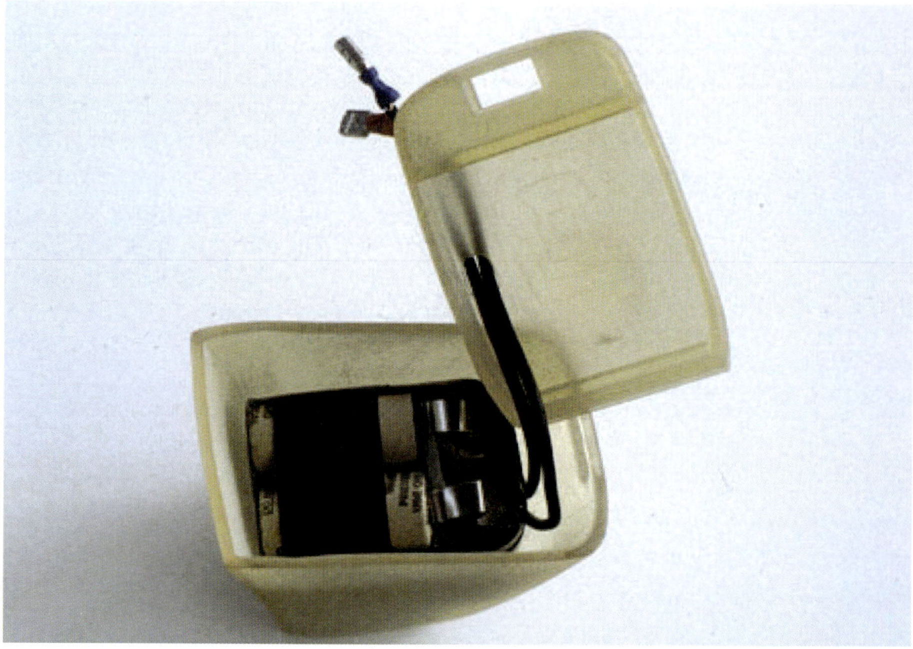

Figure 10 Battery compartment and lid for the nylon-line grass trimmer produced using stereolithography

1.9 Appearance models

As accurate representations of product form, appearance models enable the client and others to evaluate the *look* of a design proposal more accurately than with renderings. Appearance models are produced in workshops by highly skilled model makers using a range of engineering drawings. Being a labour-intensive process it is also expensive. Since the model only has to look right and not function it means the model makers can use a variety of materials and techniques so as to simulate the final appearance. Such models may use wood, metal and plastics and processes suitable for one-off items such as vacuum forming – even where the final design will be made using mass production techniques such as plastic injection moulding.

This way of working has proved itself in manufacturing industry and until the recent challenge from low-cost rapid prototyping technologies it was a widely used means of producing 3D form models. An example of an appearance model for a lawnmower produced using conventional fabrication techniques can be seen in Figure 11.

Figure 11 Conventional, non-working appearance model of a lawnmower made from wood and plastics

The qualities of appearance models produced using rapid prototyping are no different from those produced using conventional fabrication techniques in that both methods must result in accurate representations of form. However, whilst rapid prototyping translates the 3D CAD data into physical components, the time required to remove the stepped surface finish from all components should not be underestimated. When translating rapid prototype components into an appearance model, the process can be described as far from rapid! There is also the potential for the surface to become distorted through the removal of excessive material during smoothing which takes it away from the specification of the original 3D geometry. Despite these limitations, for complex forms, rapid prototyping can be used to produce appearance models significantly faster than when using conventional fabrication techniques. The appearance models produced using rapid prototyping for the handles of children's cutlery can be seen in Figure 12.

Figure 12 Rapid prototype handles used in appearance models for children's cutlery

1.10 Appearance prototype

The highest level of physical model produced by product design teams is undoubtedly the integration of both appearance and functionality through the appearance prototype. As the financial repercussions of design problems can be significant, appearance prototypes enable manufacturers to evaluate the product before tooling is commissioned.

Using conventional fabrication techniques, the inclusion of internal cavities and design details makes appearance prototypes considerably more expensive and time consuming to produce than appearance models. It can also be difficult to produce components that have sufficient strength to withstand the rigours of testing as many features are fabricated with adhesives. To increase durability it is possible to use a fabricated component as a pattern for vacuum casting, which uses a silicon rubber mould to produce components in a single material. This does of course add complexity, cost and time to the modelling process.

An example of an appearance prototype for the lawnmower can be seen in Figure 13.

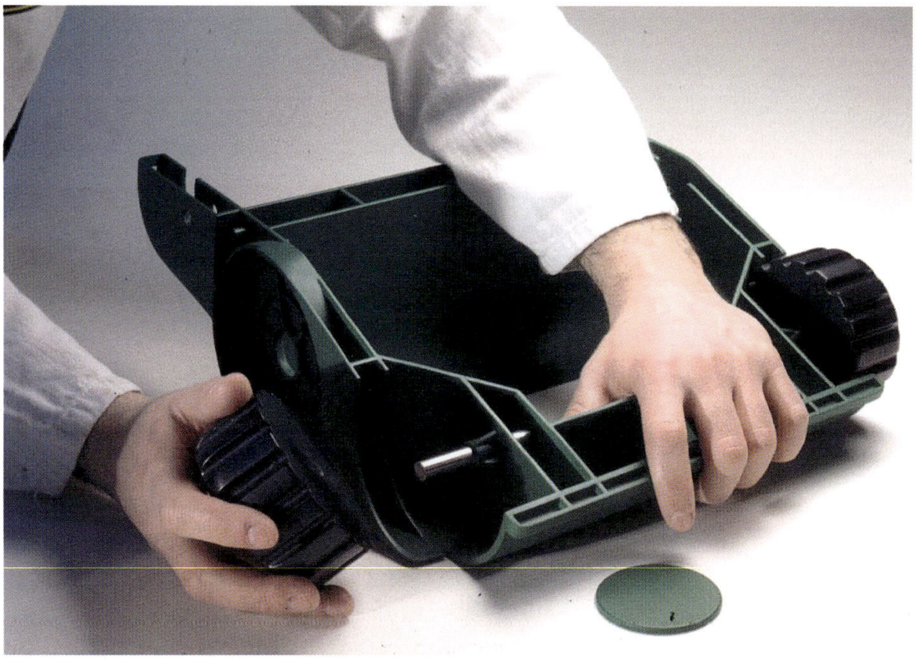

Figure 13 Assembling an appearance prototype of the lawnmower

A major advantage of rapid prototyping for appearance prototypes is that there is no significant additional cost for complex forms as costs are based on the size of components and the volume of material they require. This enables complex form and detail to be translated into physical components with relative ease once the form has been modelled in 3D CAD. There have also been significant developments in the performance of the materials used in rapid prototyping, some of which can be as strong as the materials eventually used in production.

During the design of the nylon-line grass trimmer, rapid prototyping was used in the production of an appearance prototype for testing. This was a complex product requiring the inclusion of electro-mechanical components and was subjected to high frequency vibration and robust handling. This performed extremely well in user trials and it is estimated that this was produced in one fifth of the time required for conventional fabrication techniques. The appearance prototype for the grass trimmer undergoing testing can be seen in Figure 14.

Figure 14 Appearance prototype for the nylon-line grass trimmer

1.11 Future developments

The increasing use of rapid prototyping has eroded the need for designers to make models with their own hands and some view this with concern. Critics of this development highlight the potential erosion of creativity – including the hands-on exploration of form, surface quality, and colour. Many see a real value in designers directly manipulating materials as part of the creative process and support the use of such modelling in parallel with the sophisticated capabilities of CAD. In order to address this issue, 'haptic' feedback devices have been developed to allow designers a new type of involvement in CAD processes. Haptic systems provide designers with feedback on the shapes, surfaces and textures they create on screen via an input device. A pen-like object is connected, via a linked arm, to the computer. As one moves the cursor around the virtual model on the screen the pen feels as if it is travelling over a real object because the computer is controlling the resistances in the pen arm. One can 'feel' the exact shape of a product plus more subtle features such as texture and softness. A further development of this technology, for example SensAble Technologies 'FreeForm' system, allows the designer to virtually sculpt form in ways not dissimilar to those of conventional techniques but with the advantage of producing a full 3D digital model. The SensAble FreeForm system can be seen in Figure 15.

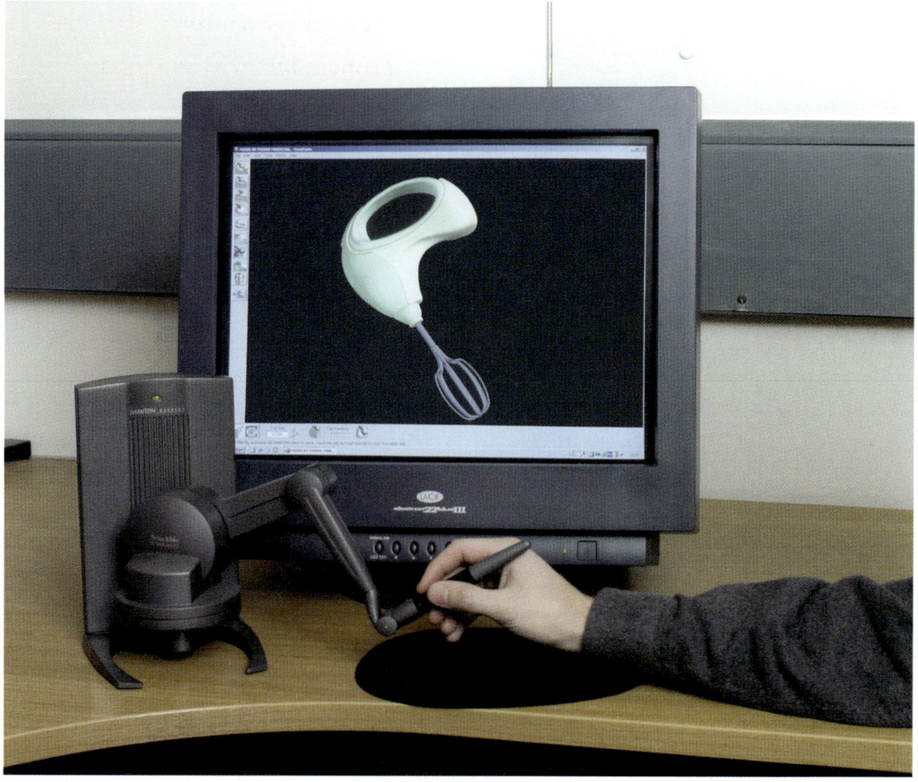

Figure 15 SensAble 'FreeForm' haptic feedback device allows users to create, modify and interact with (or 'feel') their virtual models

Emerging digital design techniques appear to have the potential to make a contribution to future product design methods. Techniques such as virtual prototyping (for entire engineering systems), virtual manufacturing (after virtual prototyping) and virtual assembly may reduce the quantity of physical models required thereby reducing the time from concept to product launch. Research into the automation of the design process threatens to remove the product designer altogether through the use of neural networks that manipulate a product specification within design parameters to produce proposals.

My thoughts on this essay are given in Box 1. You might like to record any further thoughts you have on it in your workfile once you have completed SAQ 1.

Box 1 The use of models in product design

The essay by Evans provides a useful summary of models used in product design. For me, there are three key observations:

1. Design projects give rise to a variety of models and each is used at a different stage. We have seen:

    concept sketches;
    sketch renderings;
    conventional renderings;
    3D rough models;
    principle-proving models;
    working models and prototypes;
    3D computer aided design (CAD);
    rapid prototyping;
    appearance models;
    appearance prototypes.

2. Each type of model has its own advantages and disadvantages:
    (a) sketch constructions and drawings contain very little information but they can be very fast to produce and thus they are good for supporting creative activity where many ideas need to be explored quickly (this is picked up in Block 3).
    (b) detailed models of components or assemblies of components might allow thorough evaluation but they can take a long time to build and be expensive.

3. We have seen the use of 'virtual' models built with CAD software and 'physical' models such as appearance models and appearance prototypes. Traditionally, manufacturers and design consultancies have restricted these detailed modelling types to the later stages of design activity when the concept has been approved and they are sure of the value of their investment in time and resources. However, with easy to use and low cost systems for generating virtual models we are seeing radical changes in the practice of design – not just in product design, engineering design and architecture but also in graphic design, fashion design and furniture design. Virtual models can now be easily converted to physical models via any one of several rapid prototyping techniques (explored in Block 5). If designing is partly the iterative process of generating and evaluating models then it seems that computer based techniques have already made significant inroads to improving the quality and the speed of designing.

SAQ 1

Produce a chart like the one overleaf (you may need to make the rows and columns bigger). Add your own notes on 'description', 'advantages' and 'when used' for each model type.

Can you recall the picture Mark Evans used to illustrate each model type? You might find it useful to note the figure number of each.

Model type	Description	Advantages	When used
concept sketches	Mostly line drawings. Perspective or view of side, plan etc.	Quick and cheap way of conveying basic information	Very early stages of design
sketch renderings			
conventional renderings			
3D rough models			
principle-proving models			
working models and prototypes			
3D computer aided design (CAD)			
rapid prototyping			
appearance models			
appearance prototypes			

2 Making your mark

2.1 But I can't draw!

Some people can draw very well. They seem able to capture an amazing likeness of people, places, or objects on paper. But it's not my intention to teach you how to be an artist. My aim is much more modest – to help you to develop skills and knowledge of design drawing. Drawings are valuable in design because they can represent the visual form of so many of the objects we find around us – whether this is a design for a magazine page, an item of clothing or a motorcycle.

There are two basic reasons why we might want to use drawing in our designing:

Firstly we might want to record, save or document decisions that have been made. At the end of design activity the product will need to be communicated to those who must make it. Manufacturers keep drawings of every component of every product they make. These will be very specific and detailed drawings. They allow people to issue precise instructions, for example, regarding the manufacture, assembly or quality required.

But drawings are also used in the process of creating. As you have seen in the essay by Evans, sketches and rough models are made *during* the design activities and *before* an artefact is brought into being.

We are going to explore a few techniques that will assist you to use drawing for both these functions but the emphasis is on the latter. The activities aim to improve your communication, to help you clarify and externalise your design thinking and perhaps be more creative. In short, sketching will help you be a better designer.

Some people have great powers of verbal or written communication but that doesn't seem to put off the rest of us from using speech and writing in our normal day-to-day activities. So why should we be so reluctant to make drawings? The trouble is that many of us have become very self-conscious of our drawing ability. From the early years of adolescence we judge our drawings and if they fail to match the qualities of the work of the 'artists' in our classroom many of us resolve never to embarrass ourselves by putting pen or pencil to paper for anything other than writing. This is reinforced by a widespread intellectual snobbery that suggests that verbal language, and the mental capacities that support it, are nearly always superior to drawing and the cognitive skills on which that mode of communication is based. Until recently, our education system ignored the value of drawing in all but the earliest years. It's not surprising then, that so many of us begin our adult lives with little knowledge of drawing, little experience of drawing and little confidence in our drawing abilities.

Let's start to put that right with some basic drawing activities.

Most of the activities appear as video sequences on the DVD. You can watch these at any time to help you set up your equipment, complete the task or assess your output.

Activity 1 The daily sketch

Toolkit

An inexpensive ball-point pen.

A newspaper

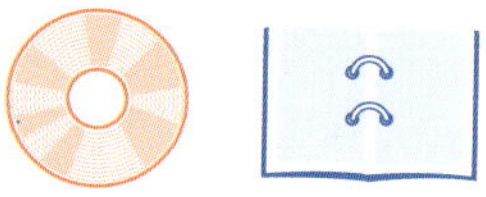

One of the problems with learning to draw lies in our fear of 'getting it wrong'. For some there is a fear of spoiling the paper or wasting resources. Often this fear is combined with not knowing where to start. This activity addresses these fears.

I want you to use an old newspaper to draw on and any cheap pen to draw with. A ball-point pen of any colour will do fine. Turn to an inside page and draw 4 or 5 square and rectangular boxes on one page and across text and photographs; see Figure 16(a). Draw these freehand and quite quickly. By 'freehand' I mean without the use of a ruler or other straight edge to guide the pen. Aim to make your boxes somewhere between 3 cm x 3 cm and 6 cm x 6 cm in size.

Now, I want you to use these boxes to demonstrate control of your pen. In each box devise and draw freehand a series of parallel lines that we might refer to as 'cross-hatching'. Each box should contain different styles of cross-hatching – lines can be vertical, horizontal or diagonal. Don't scribble your pen aimlessly back and forth – try to achieve straight, parallel lines of even line weight and thickness. Within any one box the line spacing should be as even as your judgement allows but you may use different line spacings in different boxes.

Finally, in each of these cross-hatched boxes I want you to draw one or two letters that you can copy from any headline in the newspaper. Try to achieve exactly the same shape of letterform as the originals and where possible try to make the letter or letters the full height of each box; see Figure 16(b). Start with a feint outline of the letters and when you are happy with their proportions you can press harder with your pen to make the letter stand out from the cross-hatching. You may need to go over your outlines a few times. Now make your letter stand out boldly by filling in the letters using more cross-hatching – the lines can be quite close to achieve a dark tone.

Figure 16(a)

Figure 16(b)

There's a lot happening in Activity 1. You are:

- exploring the mark-making potential of the pen;
- learning to control your fingers and wrist and the weight of your hand during drawing;
- looking closely at the shape of letter forms;
- making judgements about the proportion and look of your own drawings.

If some drawings haven't worked, it doesn't matter. The paper can go into the bin before anybody else sees it! I deliberately asked you to use newspaper for two important reasons:

Firstly, the text and pictures provide a grid of lines, which helps you to draw vertical and horizontal lines.

Secondly, you might be more relaxed about drawing on newspaper because you can't 'spoil it' – it has low value. Drawing on a new, clean sheet of white paper can frighten even the most experienced of drawers!

What you have achieved is an engagement in the 'process' of drawing, even if the products are not always to your satisfaction. Learning to draw is about learning to enjoy the process and not to be overly concerned with the products – the drawings – that result. Gradually these will improve with practice and with confidence.

I referred above to 'looking closely at shapes' and this little skill is very important in drawing and, on a wider scale, in designing. It may strike you as strange to refer to 'looking' as a skill but as designers we need to train our eyes and minds to not simply look at the world around us but to really see – to understand the curve of a door handle, the proportions of a building, the contrast of two colours. Only by being visually aware will we be able to read and appreciate the subtle design decisions of others.

The ball-point pen (biro)

The humble ball-point pen can be classed as one of the significant products of the twentieth century. It was an invention of the Hungarian émigré Laszlo Biro in 1938 but since this time it has moved from being an expensive accessory to a disposable item. It is now so cheap to produce, and so many surround us, that we may use several in a day without giving it a thought. Even the cheapest ball-point pen can produce some characterful sketches and it is frequently used to capture quick, fleeting ideas or to make sketches that assist designers to communicate with each other. The covers of telephone directories often reveal a collection of ball-point pen doodles, many made without conscious effort by telephone users, which convey the richness and variety of the medium. Add a few inexpensive ball-point pens to your modelling toolkit (personally, I prefer to use ones with black ink).

2.2 Drawing as mark-making

To the casual observer drawing is about making lines. Making lines with a pencil on paper, making lines with chalk on a blackboard or perhaps making lines using a stick on a sandy beach. But if we look at a small selection of sketched drawings we see that 'lines' can be a diverse range of marks.

Figure 17 Drawings as 'lines'

Some marks are indeed linear but others are short and repetitive, creating the illusion of a texture. Other marks result from one long side-to-side movement. Some marks seem to have been made with speed while others seem to convey a slow and careful approach. Also, the marks seem to convey 'weight' – some are heavy and intense while other marks seem to be the result of a pen or pencil that barely touched the paper. Sketch drawing is more than merely making lines. It is expressive mark-making. It is your engagement in a process that is partly directed by you and partly directed by the pens, pencils, papers and other media that you choose to use.

2.3 Mark-making with pencils

Let's look at the qualities of a familiar sketching tool – the pencil. Modern pencils are made from a mixture of graphite and clay encased in a wooden shaft. They contain no lead at all! They are cheap and readily available in a variety of grades from very hard to very soft – the more clay in the mix the harder they will be.

The very soft pencils lose their sharpness quickly but they can be used to make a dense black mark on the drawing surface. The higher proportion of graphite means these marks can be deliberately worked, for example, by smudging with the finger or an eraser, to create effects. These softer pencils can be immediately identified by the letter 'B' (for black) which is printed on the pencil shaft. They are available from 1B (or just 'B') right up to 9B – the higher the number the softer they are. Similarly, the harder pencils bear the letter 'H' (for hard) and these too are available from 1H (or just 'H') up to 9H, which is the hardest. 2H and 3H pencils used to be widely used for engineering drawing but today most plans are produced on computer and printed out.

Pencil grades above 4H produce a thin black line, which easily indents most normal drawing papers. These very hard pencils are mostly limited to specialist applications such as drawing on stone.

Figure 18(a) depicts the range and suggests some possible applications for the pencil grades.

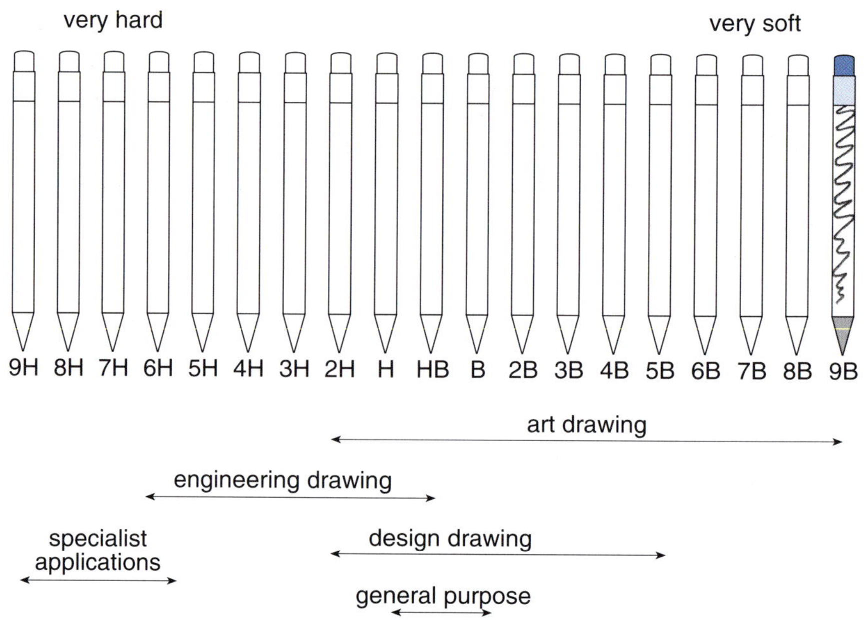

Figure 18 (a) Grades of pencil and potential applications

I suggest you add a small selection of pencils to your modelling toolkit – perhaps 2H, HB, 2B, and 4B grades, and test them by making some marks at appropriate places on the chart in Figure 18(a). I've done the 9B as an example.

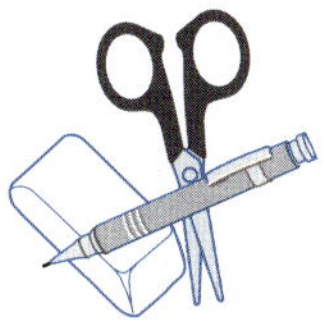

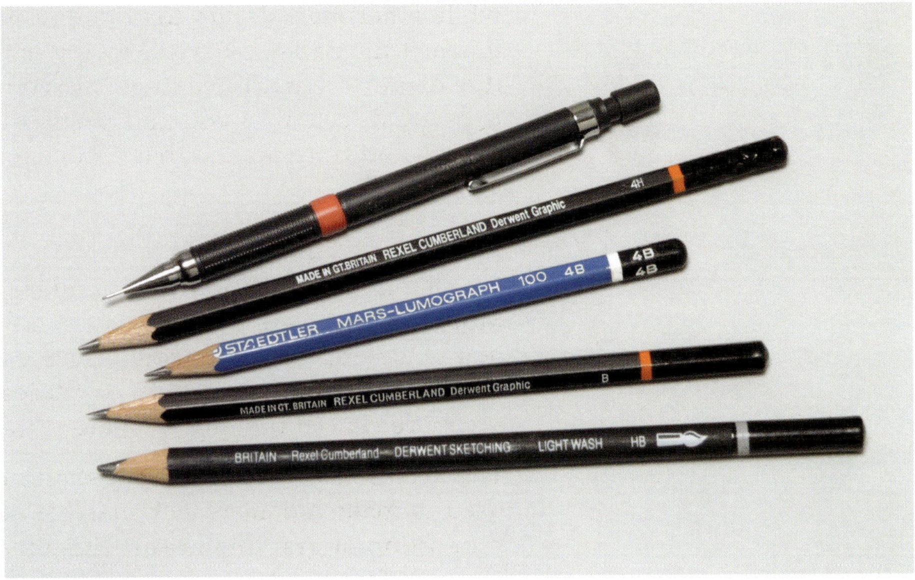

Figure 18 (b) A selection of wooden and propelling pencils

Figure 19 Example of a sketch made using a water soluble pencil

In my toolkit I have some traditional pencils but I also have a few inexpensive propelling pencils (pencils that contain a mechanism for propelling a fine lead in small incremental steps). The advantage of a propelling pencil is that it gives a more consistent line width without regular sharpening – useful if working up quick sketches of components or assemblies. This is in contrast to the traditional pencil that is sharpened to give a wide variety of tips from a broad chisel-shaped tip to a fine point. This might be useful in, for example, expressive drawing where you might want a more varied range of marks.

Water-soluble pencils are also available. After you have used these to make your sketch you can work it with a paintbrush and clean water to develop grey tones as if they were paint (Figure 19).

For most sketching activity try to keep your pencil sharp because in this way you have control over the marks it makes – a blunt pencil provides a very limited range of marks. Personally I like to use a modelling knife to sharpen my pencils because it gives me more control over the type of drawing tip available but you may prefer to use a pencil sharpener.

Activity 2 Tone and texture

Toolkit

Two–three sheets of scrap plain paper (A4)

A soft pencil (grade 3B–6B)

A medium pencil (HB or B)

A hard pencil (grade 2H–4H)

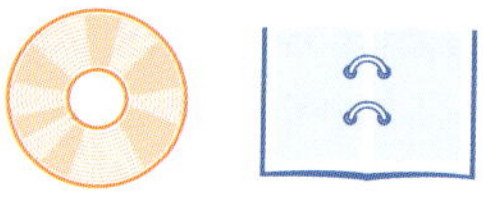

Using any sharp pencil and any plain paper draw freehand the three pencil shapes shown in Figure 20. I suggest you make each pencil approximately 8 cm long and 2 cm wide. Divide each pencil into three sections – this need not be accurate.

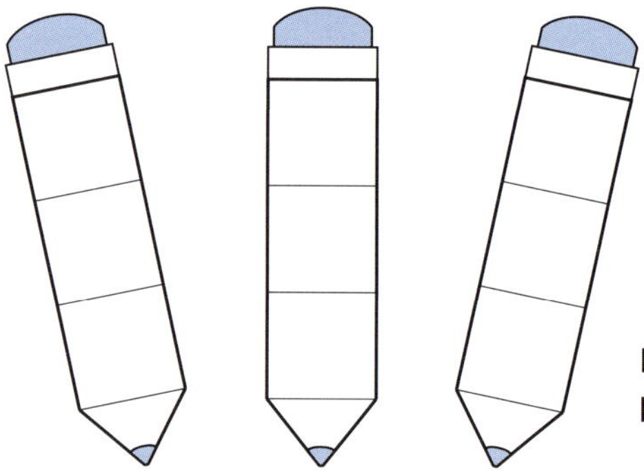

Figure 20 Three pencil shapes

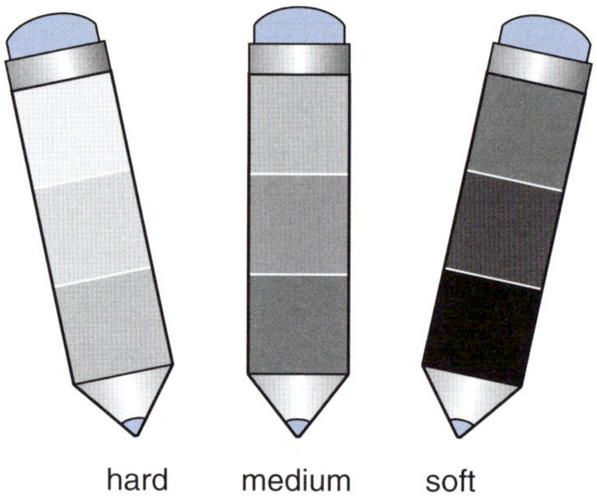

Figure 21

These will become a demonstration of pencil shading using the different grades of pencil. This is a technique for creating blocks of grey *tone* by lightly building up the graphite on the paper. You are aiming for an even tone where no lines are visible unlike the cross-hatching you did in the previous exercise. Using three pencil grades (soft, medium and hard) in turn produce a light, medium and dark tone for each pencil. The darker tones are built up by 'layering' – repeatedly going over the area – rather than by pressing very hard on the pencil. Sharpen your pencil when necessary. This activity will highlight the difference between the grades of pencil. It's quite difficult to get really smooth, even tones – don't be disappointed if yours are a bit rough.

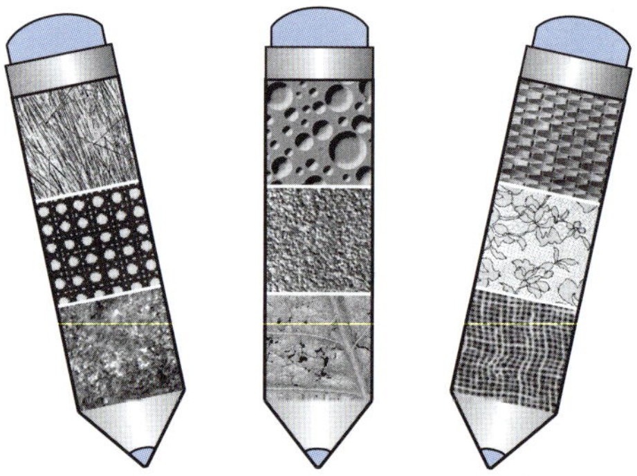

Figure 22

Draw another set of three pencils as in Figure 20. I want you to use these to document nine textures you can find around you. This works well on concrete, stone, wood grain, textured laminate, textiles, gratings and bricks. Place your paper over a texture and rub the side of a medium pencil tip over the top surface of the paper so that an impression of the texture is created through the paper – just like a brass rubbing!

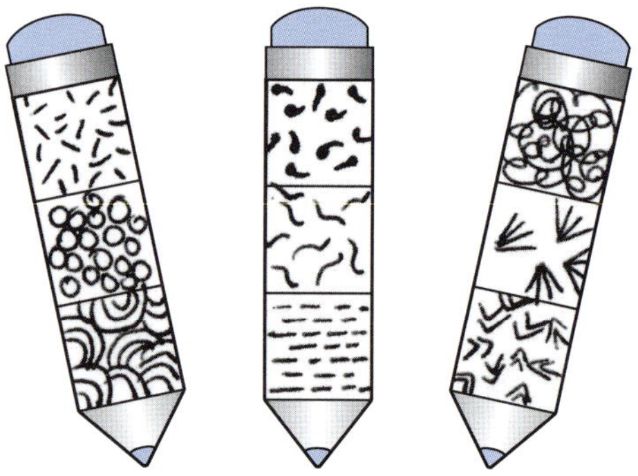

Figure 23

Finally, I want you to use a third group of pencils to show nine different types of mark you can make with your three pencils. Repeat the same mark many times to create a unique texture. These should not resemble tone or cross-hatched lines. Try short, curved marks; try holding the pencil in different ways; applying different pressures, or changing the shape of the tip by rubbing it on sandpaper or a house brick. Experiment!

The purpose of Activity 2 was to expose you to the various potentials and qualities of just one basic medium – the pencil. Each type of drawing media, whether it be coloured pencils, marker pens, charcoal etc., has its own unique qualities. If you explore and experiment you will come to understand these qualities, which in turn means you can better exploit them in your design drawing.

2.4 Using cross-hatching, tone and texture for shading

In design sketching we often want to create the illusion of *shading* on the surfaces of an object and *shadow* that is cast by an object. By adding shadow or shading with our pens or pencils we can improve the illusion of three-dimensional form – drawings seem more real. Sketches appear to stand out from the paper. In real life the light source is usually above an object (the sun or an electric light) and the shadows are below and to the sides. We normally draw it this way but we don't have to. Figure 24 shows a number of sketches of a cube drawn in pen. In this case the cube is a dice and I've used some of the techniques from Activities 1 and 2 to make it look more three-dimensional.

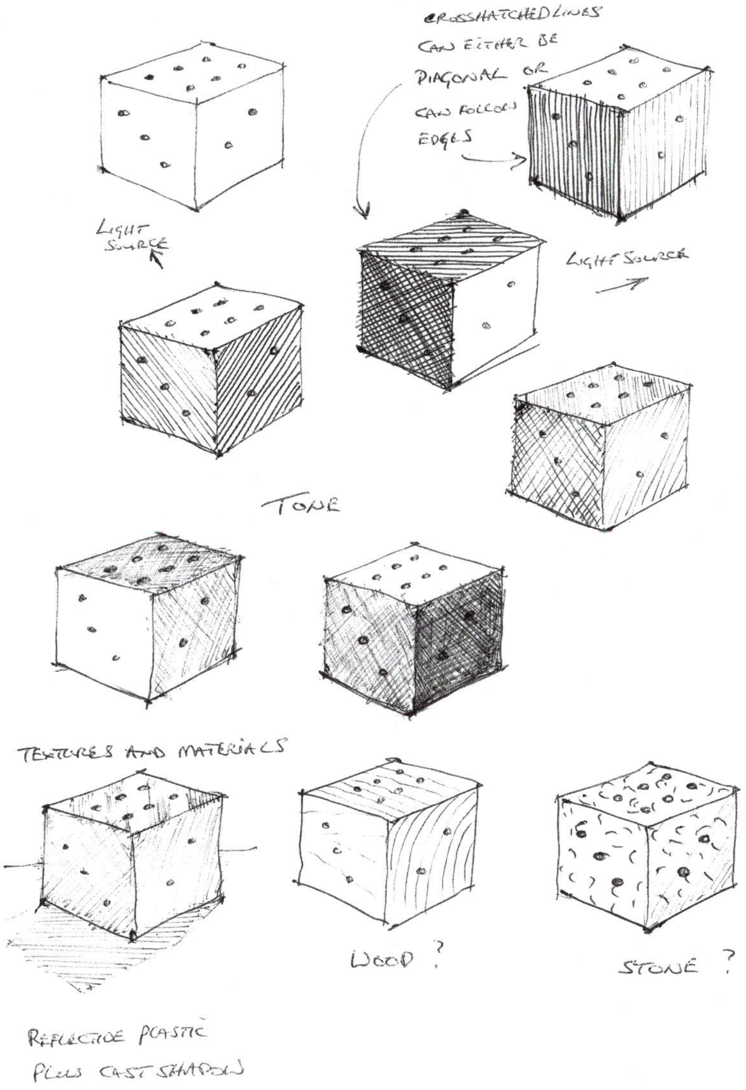

Figure 24 Sketches of a cube drawn in pen

There are light surfaces and dark surfaces to the cubes in Figure 24. Some sketches suggest light from above, other suggest the light source is to one side. The cross-hatching technique offers a crude but very quick suggestion of shade. The building up of tone takes longer but can give a stronger effect. I've used my pen to suggest various materials as well as convey shading. One sketch includes the shadow cast by the dice on the surface on which it stands. We rarely need to include this level of detail in design sketches.

You'll see more examples of the use of shading later in this workbook and you will be drawing your own perspective cubes in Sections 4 and 6.

2.5 Erasers

I've said nothing about erasers yet. Some people seem to spend as long rubbing out as drawing! Hopefully the first activity on drawing with a ball-point pen on newspaper inspired a more relaxed approach. In some respects an eraser is an important part of your modelling toolkit but don't be worried about mistakes – remember this is design sketching and not art.

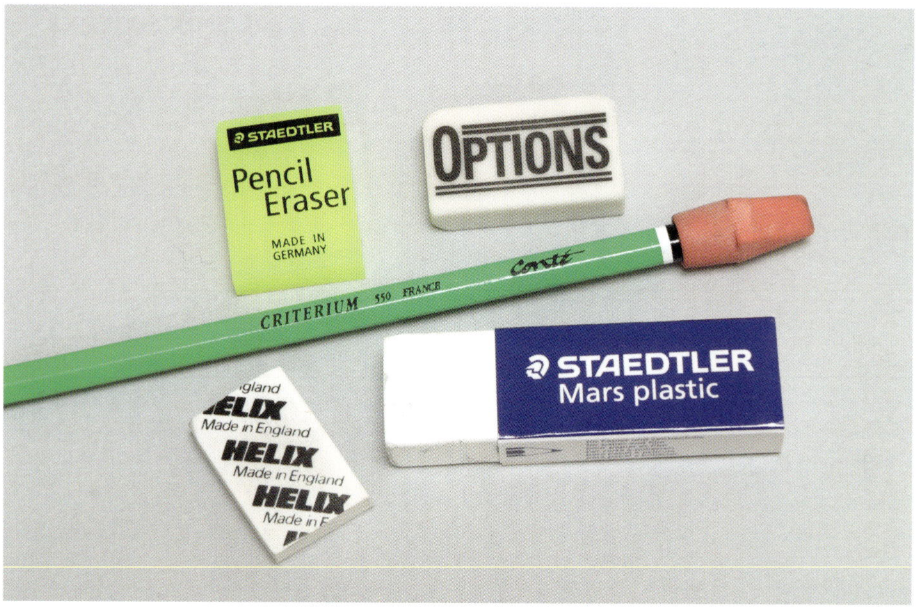

Figure 25 A selection of erasers

I have collected a variety of erasers over the years, many I've cut with a knife to give particular profiles that allow me to remove small parts of drawings. This can be very effective when used with an eraser shield – a thin metal or plastic plate used to cover part of a drawing while leaving other parts exposed to the eraser.

Some pencils and propelling pencils have an eraser built into the top. This is important as well as useful, as it encourages us to draw with confidence in the knowledge that it is ok to rub out the bits that don't work and try them again.

Erasers are not only used for removing lines, marks and tone – they can be used to produce all sorts of creative effects in drawings.

Whether your eraser is a pliable 'putty' variety, a plastic eraser or one based on a traditional rubber compound I encourage you to experiment with the ways you can modify your pencil drawings. Try it now to merge, smudge or fade the pencil textures and tones you created earlier.

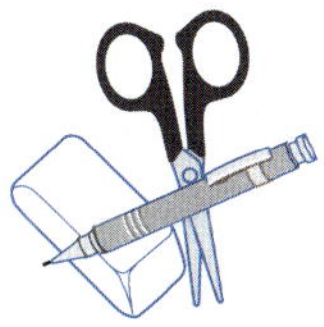

Pencil erasers

Add at least one pencil eraser to your modelling toolkit. It should rub out pencil marks without damaging the surface of the paper and without leaving streaks of graphite.

Section 2 has focussed on the making of graphic marks and sketching but of course, as you saw in the opening essay, design models can take the form of three-dimensional (3D) constructions as well as two-dimensional (2D) images. The next section explores 3D rough modelling for design and we'll return to drawing in Section 4.

3 3D rough models

3.1 A spectrum of 3D model types

In the opening essay Mark Evans presented a variety of 3D models. We could imagine these as a spectrum of modelling types ranging from the quick, cheap and simple – those Evans referred to as 'rough' models – at one end of the spectrum to the time-consuming, expensive and complex at the other end. It is normal to find rough modelling techniques exploited where design ideas may change radically whereas the more costly or labour-intensive modelling techniques are often reserved until the concept design is agreed.

3D models allow designers to progress a concept from existing merely as a graphic image to one that has a real and tangible form. People tend to understand 3D models much more easily than drawings. Such models can encourage feedback, say from potential buyers or from manufacturers, well before any significant investment in tooling or manufacturing. Rough models can be made as easily and quickly as sketches and some designers like to make rough models at the earliest stages of design. In fact, if necessary, rough modelling can begin *before* sketching. Some designers make principle-proving models before sketching.

3.2 What 'scale' should I make my models?

The subject of 'scale' is as important to design drawings as 3D models. As the makers of drawings and constructions we can decide whether we want them to be bigger than life-size, smaller or the same. There are advantages and disadvantages to each option. Some 3D models are built life-size and these can be helpful in assessing ideas because people can interact with them as they might with the final design. In fields such as consumer product design or the cutlery design you saw in the opening essay the products are relatively small and are therefore easy to model life-size. Other fields such as architecture rarely build life-size models! The constructions and drawings are mostly scaled-down versions of the intended reality. It can be very expensive to build full-size models of large designs but sometimes this has to be done where realistic user trials are required, for example in train carriage design or a control room layout.

Scale models in the form of drawings and constructions can be very helpful in design. They might be exactly half the size of the proposed design or one fifth; one tenth; one hundredth. These are sometimes described as fractions such as ½ full size and so on, or as ratios respectively 1:2, 1:5, 1:10, 1:100. In fact they could be any scale depending on the size of the product and the level of detail required in the model. Similarly scale models might be bigger than the product. I recently saw a 3D scale model of the inner workings of the human ear in a shop selling hearing aids. This model was twelve times bigger than a real human ear (12:1) because its aim was to make the anatomy clear. The activities in this workbook will assist you to make drawings and constructions at life- or full-size (1:1) and others that result in scaled-down versions of reality.

3.3 3D rough models

There can be considerable differences between 3D rough models in their look, materials, scale or size but they possess a common feature – they are relatively quick and cheap to produce.

Figure 26 Full size rough model of an electric city car intended for preliminary trials with potential users

The physical presence of rough models can require much less interpretation than, say, a sketch drawing which might make demands on viewers ability to understand perspective or other graphic conventions. Rough models produced at full-scale are particularly useful when feedback is required from users or other non-designers, for example, the car in Figure 26. Many people find it difficult to assess a scale model. Asking them to go through a sequence of activities with a full-size rough model is often much more revealing. Rough models that offer a miniature of reality (scale models) are more frequently seen when designers are exploring a concept – where they are giving form to their own thoughts rather than seeking feedback from others. In Block 3 you will see some scale models made during the design of the Moulton small wheel bicycle.

Figure 27 Rigid cellular foam models made during concept design of a digital video camera

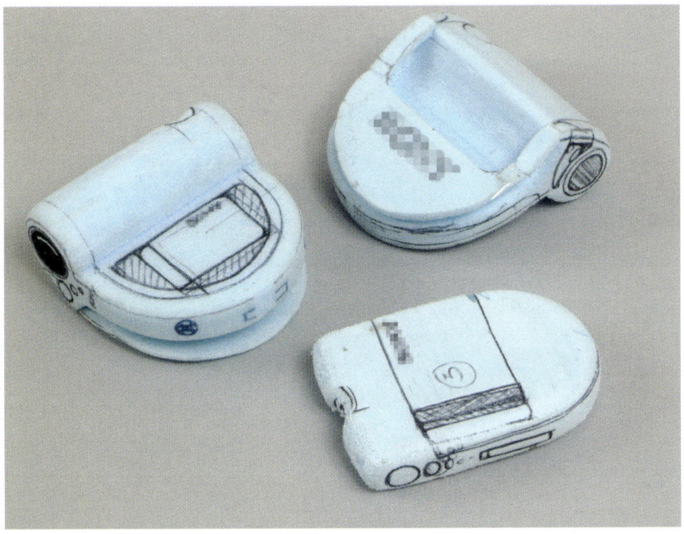

Rough models have particular value at the early conceptual stage of design when the problem, in the form of a design specification, may still be vague or deliberately open-ended. Comments or thoughts generated as a result of rough modelling can improve the specification of a design problem and support the exploration of potential ideas for addressing this problem.

The 3D rough models shown in Figure 27 were made by a student of industrial design during the early stages of a design project on digital video cameras. The models represent different ideas for resolving the same design brief. They are all modelled full-size in rigid cellular foam.

Rigid cellular foam

This is widely used in design offices because it is light, readily available from plastics suppliers, and is easily cut and shaped with simple tools as well as with machines. Sandpaper or glasspaper can be used to create smooth round forms but the cellular texture is always visible. Thick slabs of this rigid cellular foam can be stuck together for modelling large objects.

The foam models shown in Figure 27 were constructed quickly without explicitly following any detailed plan. Some of the models were guided by very basic sketch drawings (showing main outlines, side view and front view), others were formed with no reference to any drawings, rather like a sculptor might carve out a figure. You can see that the models present only the basic overall form. They contain very little other information. They do not attempt to convey the colour, texture or weight of the product. Such models might be supplemented by bits of real equipment such as headphones or mini discs in order to increase the 'realness' of the foam model.

In this example the rough models were performing a very similar function to sketch drawing. They were enabling the designer to receive feedback and to simultaneously explore both the problem and ideas for resolving it.

Let's do some rough modelling!

Activity 3 Chair model in card

Toolkit

Some thin cardboard (such as an empty cereal packet). Avoid corrugated or thick card for this modelling activity

Pencil (any)

Ruler (showing millimetres)

Scissors

Adhesive tape (e.g. masking tape)

If needed:

photocopy of the components

paper paste or glue

Block 1 focuses on seats and aspects of their design so this modelling activity involves making a scale model of a simple chair. All the components of the chair are provided for you in the plan below (Figure 28). I have made it one tenth full size (1:10) and all you need do is follow the instructions to achieve your 1:10 scale model.

1. Transfer the plans – the three rectangular shapes – onto cardboard. You can do this in two ways. Either photocopy the page (the same size) and glue this to a sheet of thin card (an empty cereal packet would be fine) or alternatively, redraw them onto the card. All the dimensions you need are given in Figure 28.
2. Cut the three rectangles out of the cardboard with a pair of scissors. Try to cut as accurately as possible along the lines.
3. Score along the dotted line on the seat/back component. To do this place the ruler against the dotted line and pull the point of your scissors along this edge. Now the card should fold accurately along this line to form the seat and back.
4. Finally assemble your chair by sticking the folded seat/back to the two side supports. Use adhesive tape for this. The guidelines on the two sides should help you stick the seat/back in the correct place. (I've placed my tape on the underside.)
5. Your model should look like Figure 29.

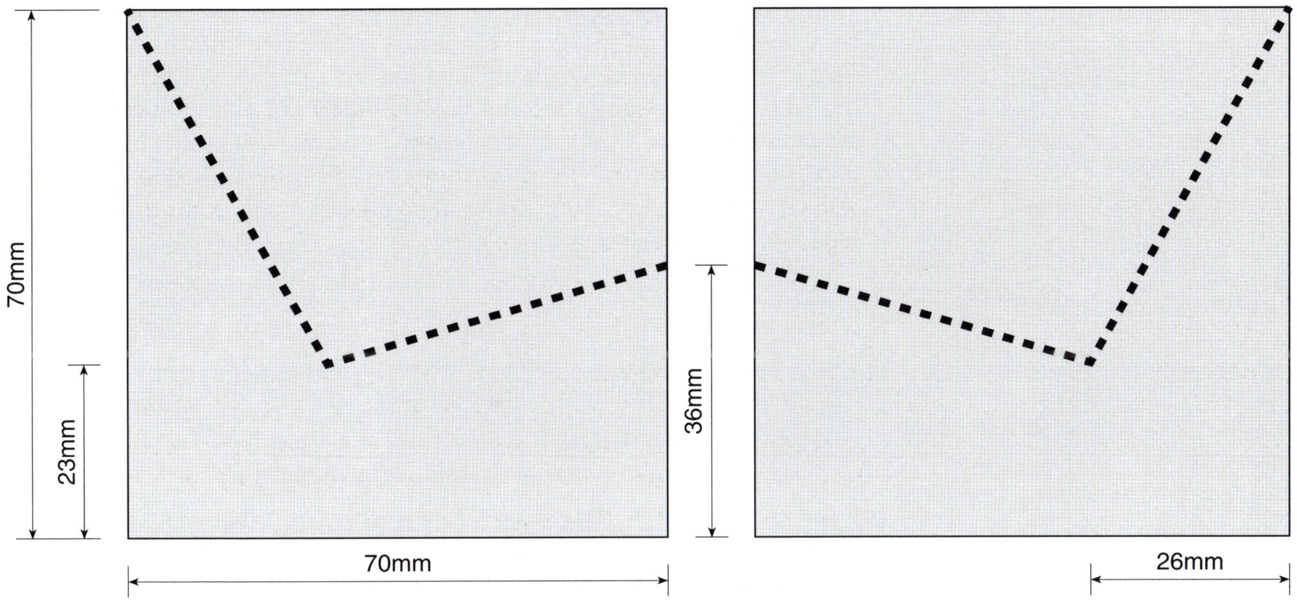

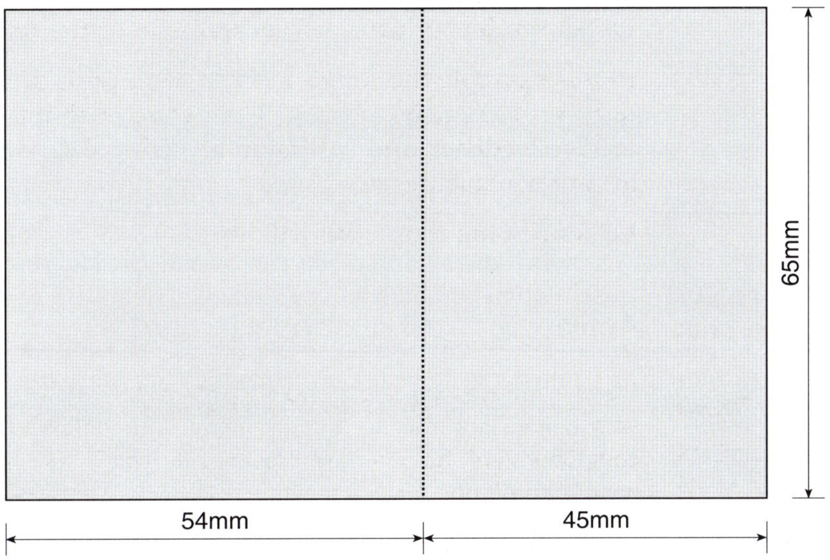

Figure 28 Components for seat model

Do you like the chair design? Identify two good points about this design and two weaknesses of the design. Show your chair model to another person and ask them to identify a few strengths and weaknesses in the design (not your modelling skills).

Even a simple rough model like this can generate a rich and creative design dialogue.

Figure 29 The 1:10 scale model of the seat

You now have a 3D rough model of a chair at the scale 1:10. Keep this card model because you will use it in a sketching activity later.

This 3D model suggests some useful qualities in the design of the chair:

- **Material qualities**: it uses only one type and thickness of flat sheet material. If a full size chair was to be manufactured a company would only need to stock one type and thickness of board, e.g. 12 mm plywood or 15 mm medium density fibreboard (MDF).
- **Functional qualities**: it presents a potentially comfortable seat and back for sitting. It acknowledges leg lengths and body sizes for a large percentage of the market.
- **Mechanical qualities**: the seat and back can be fixed to the sides to potentially offer a strong and rigid structure.

We could convert this concept to a full-size chair by redrawing it full-size onto plywood, MDF or other flat sheet material (multiplying all the dimensions in Figure 28 by ten) and cutting it out with a saw by hand or machine. Of course, we would need to design or specify the fixings to hold the seat and back to the sides but I'm going to return to this later.

Activity 4 Basic CD packaging

Toolkit

A CD (compact disc)

Some thin cardboard (such as a large empty cereal pack)

Scissors

Ruler (showing millimetres)

A sharp pencil for marking out

Paper and card glue or adhesive tape

Optional: use coloured pens or pencils to design the front and rear face of the package

This activity will familiarise you with more of the basic tools and techniques involved in card modelling. It is based around a design brief. I will assist you with some ideas so that you can quickly get into rough modelling but the design of the final model is up to you. Here's the brief:

> CD-ROMs are a very cheap and convenient way for companies to communicate with their markets. They are the preferred means of communication for companies selling holidays, cars, services etc., because of the potential to include short video clips and sound as well as pictures and text. You are asked to devise the cardboard packaging for a free CD promoting the Open University's design courses. The CD will be given away at education fairs, promotional events and posted to enquirers.

In this modelling activity you may work directly in three dimensions, that is, you don't have to sketch out your ideas on paper before you mark out your models on the card. However, if you feel you're not ready to plunge directly into designing through 3D modelling just yet then use sketching to assist you to clarify your ideas.

> Read 'My response' below before beginning your own modelling.
>
> If you are new to making models in card you might find it helpful to copy what I did but feel free to develop your own idea if you want to.

My response

My first idea for this brief was for a rather conventional envelope but in card. I made it in the following way:

1 A CD has a diameter of 120 mm and I allowed for 5 mm of space in the packaging. So first I marked out a double square measuring 125 mm x 250 mm on the reverse side of one of my cereal packets. This will

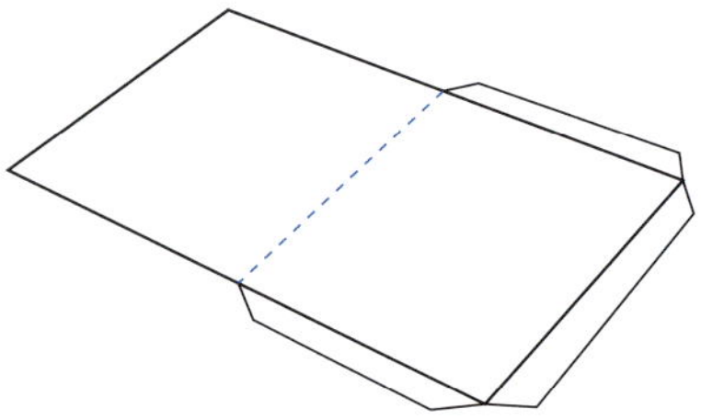

(a) Stages 1 and 2

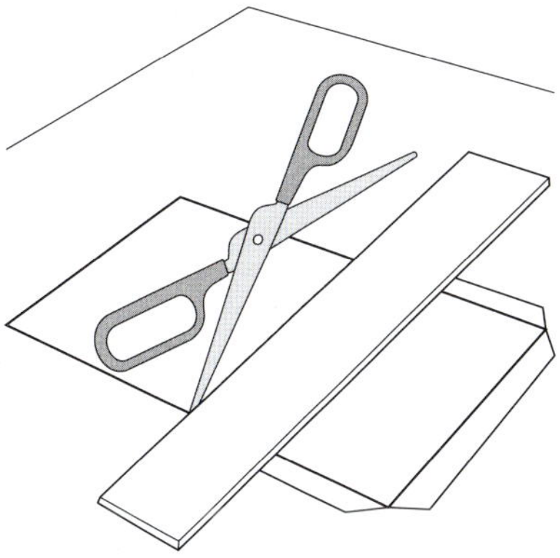

(b) Stage 3

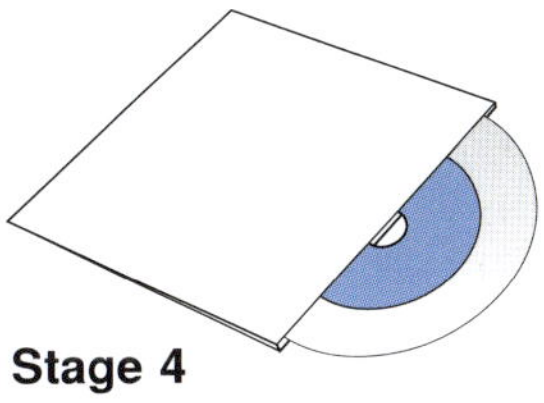

(c) Stage 4

Figure 30

become the front and rear faces of the envelope. You'll see from the illustration that I added tabs to three sides. These are 10 mm wide except for the top tab, which is 20 mm wide. This is where the package will open.

2 Cut out with scissors.

3 Now score (partially cut) those lines where folding will take place. Use the ruler and one blade of a pair of scissors as described in Activity 3. Scoring allows the card to be folded precisely thus adding accuracy to your design model.

4 Fold the two sides of the envelope together, apply adhesive to the tabs on the sides, or use adhesive tape, and stick them together. You can then – when any glue used is dry – test it with a CD.

This is a rather conventional package design and it's similar to many CD envelopes that are used today. From a design point of view the advantages are that the cutting and assembly could be easily automated, it makes economical use of material and it is suitable for being sent through the postal system. Let's try and use our modelling skills to generate and communicate more adventurous ideas.

Activity 5 A promotional CD Case

Toolkit

A CD

Plain A4 scrap paper

Some thin cardboard (such as an empty cereal packet)

Scissors and ruler

Adhesive tape or glue

A sharp pencil for marking out plus an assortment of coloured pens or pencils

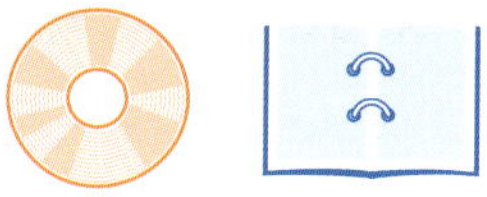

Staying with the CD packaging brief I want you to generate 3 different ideas for packaging the CD. You may want to sketch some ideas first. The objective is to produce three rough 3D models in paper and one rough card model.

Allow your ideas to emerge as you draw and make. Modify and change your ideas by adding or cutting away paper. Start again with a new piece of paper whenever you want to but don't throw away any models just yet. Many designers would use such rough models as part of their private, creative process.

When you have produced your 3D ideas in paper take a look below at the selection I have come up with in Figures 31(a)–(e).

Each of my ideas matches the brief with varying degrees of success. Some are poor ideas and I wouldn't bother taking them any further. Others seem to have potential and I might want to develop them. Some models caused me to think more deeply about the problem. For example, how thick or heavy can a package be yet still travel through the post as easily and at the same cost as an envelope? What functions might the packaging perform in addition to mere protection of the CD?

After you have looked at my ideas select one of your ideas, which you think has potential (it need not be a very good idea yet), and make it in card. You will need to devise a plan of the opened-out package. You can use your paper model to assist this.

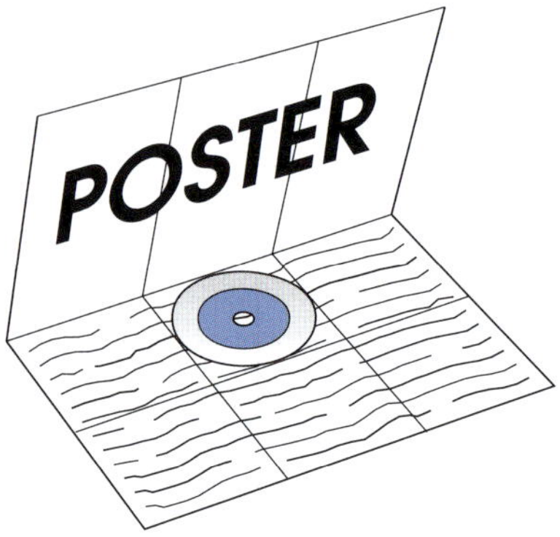

1 This idea explored the use of the packaging to fold-out, thus presenting a large surface area for information, perhaps becoming a wall poster.

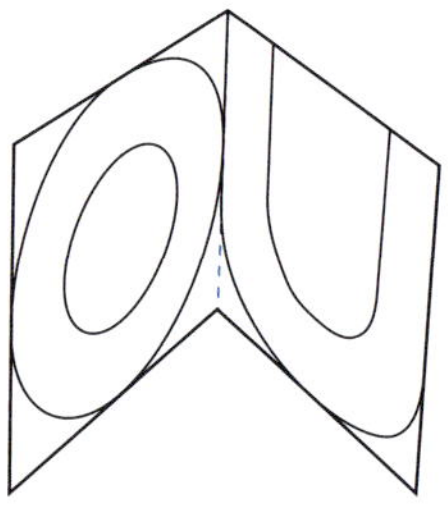

2 This idea used the letters 'OU' as inspiration for the shape of the packing, opening out like a book.

3 This globe concept sought to explore three-dimensional form. I doubt whether it would survive the postal system. Perhaps it could use an elastic band to spring open in the receiver's hand!

4 Packaging splits apart at the middle (like an egg or open mouth?)

5 Package stands up on your desk (but who has spare desk space?)

Figure 31 Some ideas for CD packaging

If some part of your design didn't work out don't worry. You could do some more development – perhaps by adding some paper or card to your rough model to improve it and then re-make it in card. It's quite normal to have to go around this iterative design cycle of making, evaluating, developing and re-making many times. In fact, this is one of the primary functions of this type of model. It supports our creativity by allowing us to externalise and test ideas quickly and cheaply.

Don't forget you can use your coloured pens and pencils to create a graphic design on this promotional CD case if you want.

Your selected idea, which you re-made in card, has one further advantage. It allows you to share your ideas with others. You can ask for their opinion of the design and receive comments on possible improvements. It has taken you a bit longer to make the card model but potentially it can generate a bit more feedback than one of the paper models. The card model is a bit easier to understand. We can make a more accurate assessment of it, for example, exactly how much card will it use or how will the users remove the CD.

Activity 6 Mug in card

Toolkit

Cereal pack or similar for cardboard

Adhesive tape or glue

Pen or pencil

Scissors

Ruler

So far we have looked at cardboard models which assist both the generation and the communication of design ideas. This exercise focuses on the development of some more model making skills but doesn't ask you to design anything.

We are going to use cardboard to make a rough model of a tea or coffee mug.

Figure 32 Photo of coffee mugs

1 Find a mug that has a simple, cylindrical form. It will be very difficult to model if it bulges, tapers or is flared at the top. See Figure 32 for some suggestions.

2 To convert this form into a flat, full-size plan first measure the height of your mug and the circumference. An easy way to measure the circumference is to wrap a strip of paper around the mug and mark where it crosses (just like taking your waist measurement with a tape measure).

3 Draw a rectangle on your sheet of card with the height of the mug as the vertical dimension and the circumference + 20 mm as the horizontal dimension (the extra 20 mm will be an overlap). Cut out this rectangle.

4 Put the mug onto some card and draw round the base. Add several tabs to the outside of this circle as in Figure 33(b) and cut out this shape. Score the lines where the tabs join the circle so that they fold easily.

5 Gently manipulate the card rectangle so that it begins to form a cylinder but *don't stick the two sides together yet.*

6. Place the circle inside one end of the cylinder. *The tabs should go inside the cylinder.* Using adhesive tape or glue stick each tab to the inside of the cylinder in turn.

7 Finally overlap the two sides and stick them together giving you a cylinder with a base – an approximation of your mug.

The handle is a little more tricky. I made mine in the following way:

8 Measure the width of the handle and estimate the overall length. Cut out three strips of card to this width. Make them longer than necessary.

9 Bend each of these to the approximate handle shape.

10 Using glue or tape, stick the curved strips together. Adjust the curvature of this handle as necessary by bending or straightening.

11 Trim the length leaving about 10 mm each end for sticking to the 'mug'. Now stick the handle to your card mug.

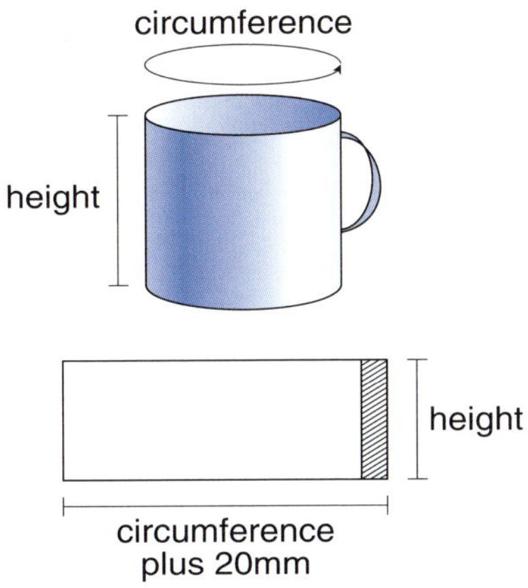

(a) Stage 3

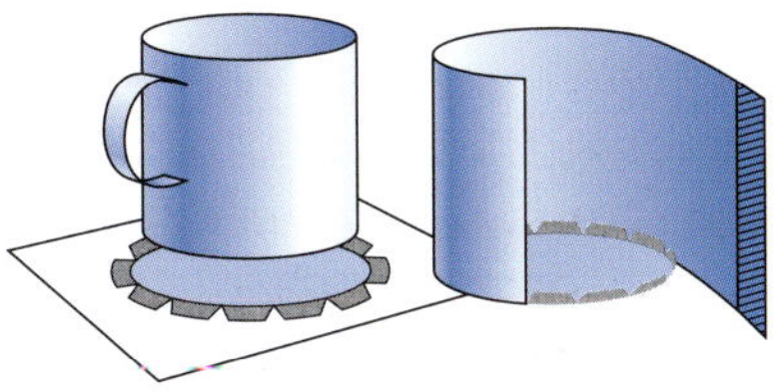

(b) Stages 4–6

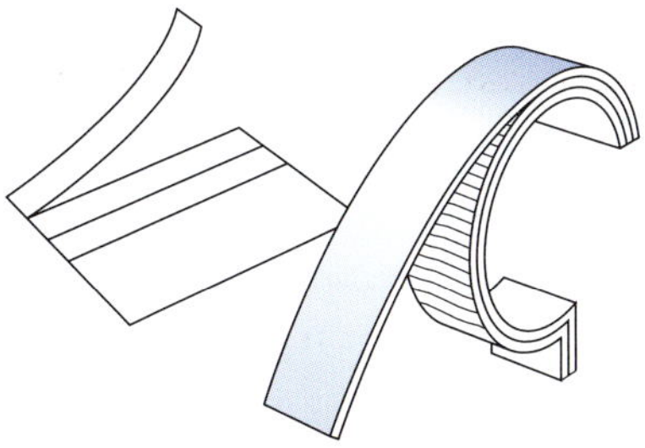

(c) Stages 8–10

Figure 33 Selected stages in making a model mug

3.4 Rough modelling in professional practice

The model of the mug you made in Activity 6 is not a pretty model by any stretch of the imagination. The construction reveals the raw cardboard, the adhesive tape, and perhaps even the graphics from the original cereal packet. It's probably not a very accurate model, revealing some distortions or errors. However, it was relatively quick and cheap to make and the basic form is clear. The model could enable you to discuss some of the intended design qualities of your mug.

Your model of the mug has its counterpart in professional design practice. Look at the rough model produced in the Dyson company as part of the early development of the DC05 vacuum cleaner (Figure 34) and compare it to the simpler forms you have made.

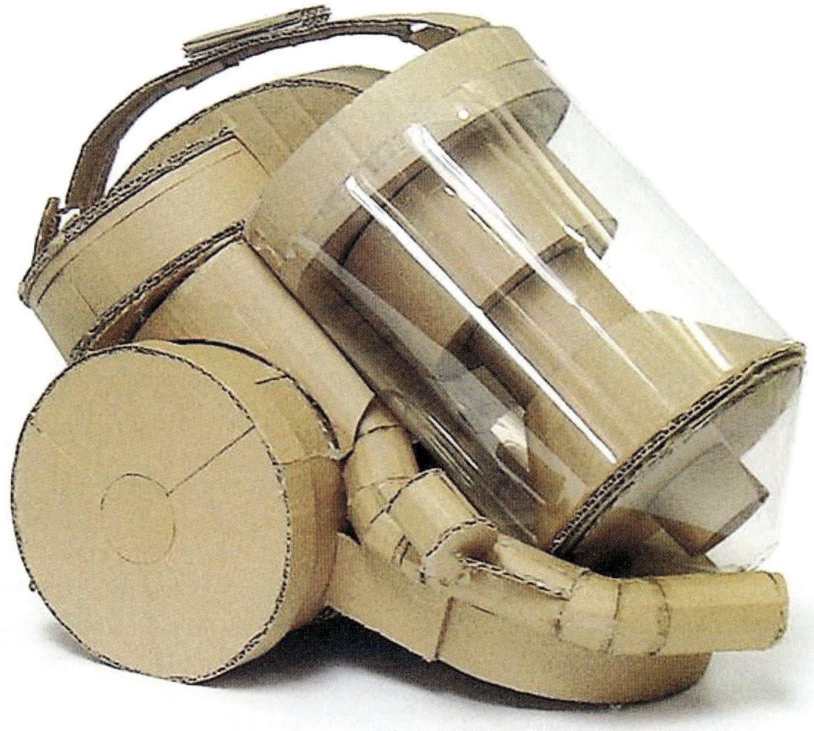

Figure 34 Dyson vacuum cleaner DC05; early development model in card

In the Dyson example the designers were using their card modelling skills to construct a life-size rough model of an idea in development. In places we see the adhesive tape which holds the model together. However, the basic geometry of the product is clear – the wheels modelled to their actual thickness, the cylinder representing the cyclone chamber, the motor housing, and the various tubes linking components together. The Dyson card model uses a piece of clear film to allow viewers to see some internal components.

SAQ 2

Full-size rough 3D models such as the Dyson vacuum cleaner model in card are very useful in design. How might this rough Dyson model be used to assist design activity?

My answer to this SAQ is given at the back of the workbook. You should try to answer this for yourself before looking at mine.

3.5 Rough modelling with malleable materials

As you may have found when you were making the handle for your mug out of cardboard, sheet material is impractical or inadequate for some modelling tasks. Ideally you want something that is 'plastic' – something you can bend and shape into complex forms. We saw at the beginning of this section the use of rigid cellular foam for the rough modelling of personal music players but there are other materials you can use. I'll use a knife handle design to illustrate this (Figure 35).

Figure 35 Knife models using handles made from various modelling materials to collect user feedback on comfort and usability

This particular project aimed to produce a kitchen knife that would function equally well for those with weak grip such as those with arthritis or age-related weakness as well as for those in the mainstream market. It may be relatively easy designing a knife for the mainstream market but it's notoriously difficult trying to design for people who have abilities and limitations different from these. Often the most important aspect of such designing is being able to fully understand the needs of the potential users and this is a central concept in Block 2 of this course. There is a need to use models which tell us something about the range of users, their capabilities and the design context in general. These are models which help us to better understand the design problem rather than allow us to communicate our ideas for resolving it.

As part of the design research a number of dummy knives were fitted with plasticine handles. These were soft enough for the researchers to modify the forms of the handles in response to the user's comments. It also allowed the participants to contribute to the design by making their own suggestions.

Once the design researchers had a suitable understanding of the design requirements a second type of rough model was used in user trials. A relatively cheap polymer, available in granular form, was softened in hot water resulting in a material resembling warm soft wax. This could be wrapped around a real knife shaft to form a shape suggested by the earlier trials with plasticine. As the polymer cools it becomes rigid. The handle and blade become tightly bonded together allowing the user trials to involve real kitchen tasks such as cutting and paring. In this way the researchers got improved feedback on the problem without spending significant amounts of time in ideas development or significant amounts of money on tooling. If these 'sketch' models need development the handle is simply immersed in hot water and the polymer reverts to its pliable, wax-like state until it once again cools.

You might want to undertake some simple studies of cutlery handles yourself. Wrap plasticine around a spoon, fork or knife. Test it on friends and family including, if possible, elderly people or children. Modify the design in response to comments. You are using modelling for identifying the problems as well as proposing solutions.

Having explored some 3D models the next section takes us back to sketching.

4 Sketching

4.1 Sketching for all

As you saw in the opening essay by Mark Evans, even with the widespread availability of computer tools commercial design practice still displays a strong attachment to freehand drawing. The aim of this section is to get you feeling confident in making design sketches.

Design sketches show only what matters for a particular design purpose. This kind of drawing is not 'showing it like it is' but requires selectivity; it requires you to be more analytical. Sometimes sketches attempt to convey accuracy in shapes, curves, proportions etc. At other times sketches can be more 'impressionistic'. If you have a background in engineering or technical drawing the new skills will probably be in making looser, more confident freehand sketches in parallel with your thinking process. Sketching can assist you to be more creative as well as assist you to share your ideas with others. This connection with creativity is further explored in Block 3.

Like anything else in life, mental or practical, design sketching only starts to come naturally and hence to become a pleasure when we put in a bit of effort. If we are going to put marks on paper that describe things we can see or things in our imagination we need to understand our media (the pens, pencils, paper etc.) as well as develop skills. Usually this combination of knowledge and skill will only come about through practice – just as a golf swing, digging the garden, or car driving need practice. You began to develop your craftsmanship with a pencil in Section 2 and in this section you are going to make actual drawings. But there is one nagging little question to get out of the way before we start...

4.2 Why not use words?

Why use drawings to describe what we mean when we have a language full of perfectly good words? OK, here are some words:

> This object is 120 mm in overall height and about the same in overall depth, front to back. It is made of a hard red plastic. Its main element is a hollow cylinder, 55 mm in diameter and 85 mm high. Inside this is a spring mechanism and out of the top of it comes a vertical post 25 mm high with a flat plate on top shaped like an elongated capital D, 55 mm × 73 mm. This plate rises and falls according to the pressure on the top of it. The flat top surface of the cylinder extends forward like a square-ended tongue 55 mm wide, which then curves downwards on the arc of a quarter circle. The flat, front-facing surface of that tongue is 10 mm thick and down the centre runs a slot in which moves a little bar. This rises and falls in the slot according to the pressure on the top plate. Up the sides of the slot are numerical scales and the whole front is enclosed in a Perspex cover.
>
> What is it?

Has the description above given you a clear impression of the object concerned? If you have any real picture in your mind at all it will probably have taken quite a lot of effort. Even then, how many dimensions and angles of an obviously quite complicated shape have really been described here? When you look at the picture of this

Figure 36 The object described in Section 4.2 – postal scales

object (Figure 36) it can feel as if a fog has been lifted. Everything vague, about which you only knew a few elementary features, now has a detailed form and you can see how the various bits relate to each other to make up the product.

Now imagine yourself on the other side; not on the receiving end of the description but faced with conveying a description of another complex object to someone else – perhaps a mobile phone or a hair dryer. It must be done, not in a vague or ambiguous way but in a way that is precise and not liable to misunderstandings. How would you describe the curved surfaces, the subtle details, the controls and displays? Suddenly drawing doesn't seem so daunting!

4.3 The representation of form and space

Design drawing can represent two-dimensional and three-dimensional subjects. Activity 1 involved you in the depiction of letter forms and for some designers their work is mostly concerned with two-dimensional outputs such as the design of a page for a magazine, a book or a website. However, in fields such as product design, engineering and architecture, drawing needs to address the problem of communicating three-dimensional forms such as consumer products, vehicles or buildings on a two-dimensional drawing surface. In these contexts drawing is merely an illusion, creating marks on paper that can be 'read' as meaning a three-dimensional form. So powerful are some of these techniques that the three-dimensionality of the images can still be read even when they have been only casually sketched.

Figure 37 Sketches can convey a powerful sense of three dimensions. Alec Issigonis, perspective sketch for the BMC Mini, 1958

The communication of three-dimensional space, and perhaps more importantly for this course the spatial relationships of components in a product, can be achieved in various ways. Some techniques have developed to provide accuracy of information so that, for example, the drawing can be used as a plan to make something. Other techniques seek to depict the object in such a way that we might easily and quickly understand general features of the object, such as its overall form, but not necessarily be able to make it. The former is concerned with precision and repeatability of information while the latter is concerned with generalisation and immediacy in the understanding of information. I'm going to engage you in activities that explore these two broad aims of representation.

Activity 7 Sketching simple views

Toolkit

A sharp pencil (HB, B or 2B)

One A4 size sheet of squared paper (from the paper pack)

The card scale model of a seat from Activity 3

Ruler

Eraser

Figure 38

In Activity 3 you produced a 1:10 scale card model of a seat (as in Figure 38). I want you to use this model in this sketching activity.

Hold the card model in front of you and look at three different views – the side, the front and from above. You are going to create sketches of these three views on the squared paper supplied in the paper pack.

1 With the front of your model pointing to your left look at it from the side. This *side view* appears in Figure 39. Measure this rectangular side with a ruler (or take the dimensions from the drawings shown in Activity 3). Now draw this rectangle, the same size, on a sheet of A4 squared paper. This must be near the top left-hand corner of the paper (because you are going to fit in two other views on this page). In this activity you can use the ruler for any measuring but I want all lines to be drawn freehand (without using the ruler) – use the 5 mm grid to guide your sketching of the horizontal and vertical lines. Add a horizontal 'baseline' to represent the surface the chair stands on.

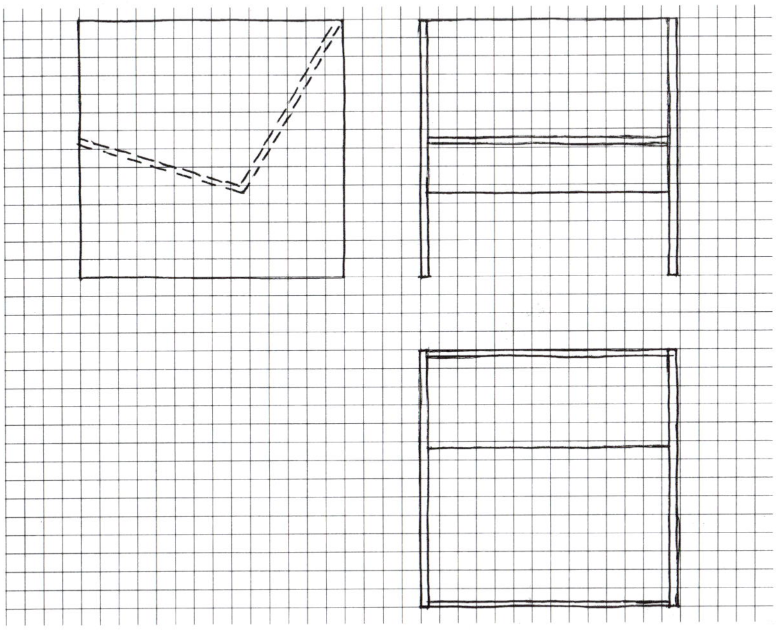

Figure 39

2 As in Figure 39 I want to show the edges of the seat and back in this side view. I can't directly see them because they are covered by the side but I can use the convention of a broken line to show their location. Either measure your chair or copy the 'left side' drawing that appears in Activity 3. Again, draw your lines freehand. Estimate the thickness of your card seat and back and sketch this thickness.

3 Now sketch the *front view* of the model to the right of your side view. You'll need to measure the width of your seat (or take the dimension from the drawings in Activity 3). You can use the side view to help you draw the heights of the seat and back if you 'project' lines across from one view to the other. The front view should sit on the same baseline as the side view. Again, use the grid to guide your sketching of all the verticals and horizontals.

4 Finally sketch the *plan view* underneath the front view. Again you can project lines down from the front view to help you place the plan view on the page and get the dimensions correct.

What you have just produced is a set of *orthographic* views of your chair model. You are broadly following set rules and conventions to produce certain views of an object. There are a number of conventions associated with orthographic drawing and I'm going to look at these in Section 5 of this workbook. For now you have done all that you need. You have produced sketches of three important views of a three-dimensional object.

Such a drawing contains, in quite a lot of detail, information about your scale model of a chair. Your drawing could be read and understood by others. In fact, there's probably enough information for someone to make a copy of your model by just using your drawing! This is often exactly what we want to achieve in design drawing.

Figure 40 shows a selection of design sketches that exploit orthographic views of their objects.

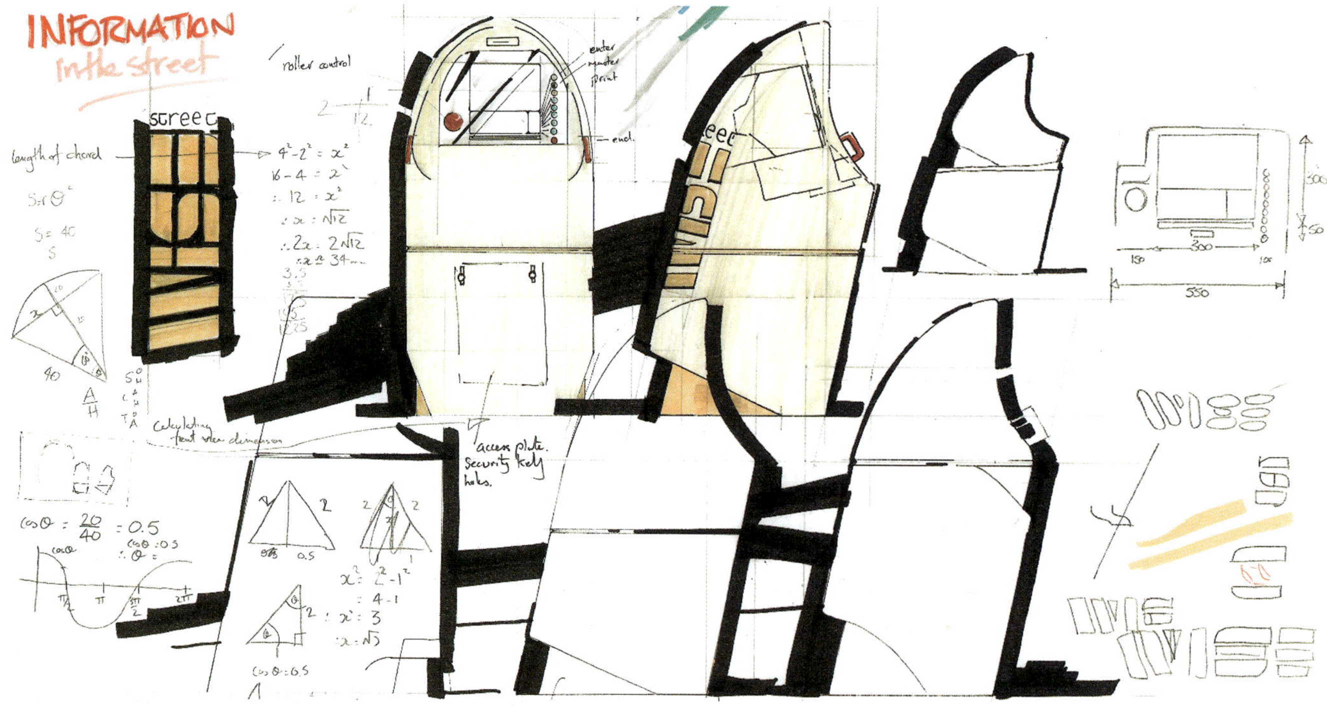

(a) street information point

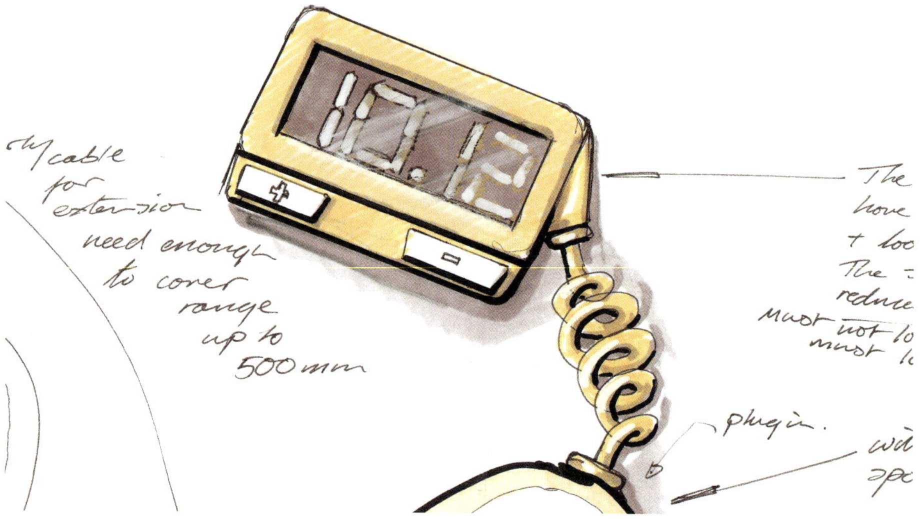

(b) digital readout for a weighing scale

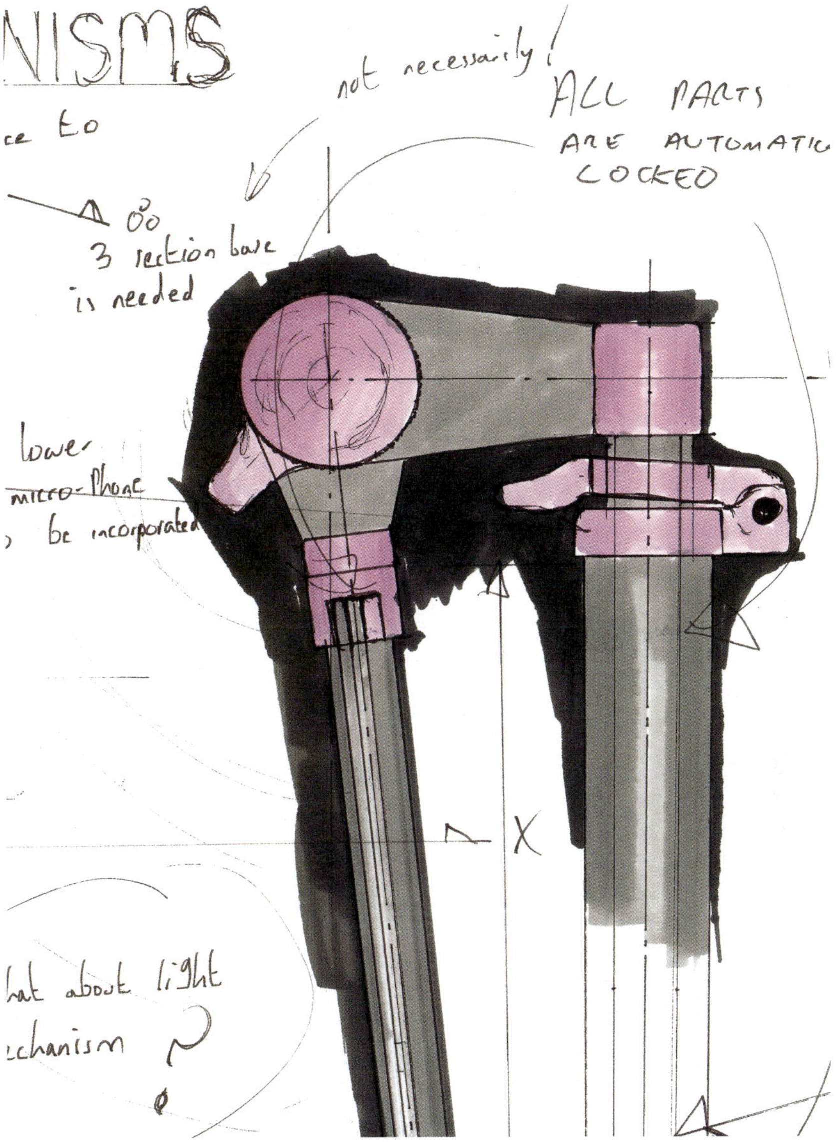

(c) folding mechanism on artist's easel

Figure 40

Before we go to the next sketching activity I want to introduce you to another type of pen – a fine-pointed ink pen that I'd like you to try using in your sketching.

4.4 Fine-point pens

Pens have been used for centuries to control the application of a pigment such as ink onto various surfaces. They differ from pencils in that pens contain a liquid or semi-liquid media and thus they need to incorporate a device which both holds back the reservoir and yet allows a predictable amount of it to pass through in use.

Figure 41 A selection of pens suitable for sketching

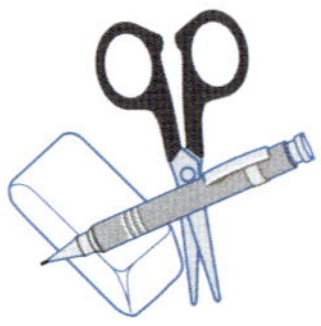

Fine-tipped technical pens are now as widely used in the home and office as ball-point pens. They have become cheap to produce, reliable and robust in use, and inexpensive to buy. They can be used to produce sensitive sketches displaying subtlety in line weight. I prefer to draw in black ink because it offers a strong contrast on white paper and I can introduce tone or colour if required. However, you may prefer to draw with blue, green, brown or red ink. A selection of low-cost, fine-point pens are included in Figure 41. I suggest you acquire one or two cheaper ones for your modelling toolkit.

4.5 Qualities in line work

Figure 42 shows a variety of sketches of chairs; these sketches were made with a selection of cheap fine-point pens. The views we see are very different to the views we constructed in Activity 7. There the aim of the orthographic sketching was to capture separate and accurate views of the front, side and plan.

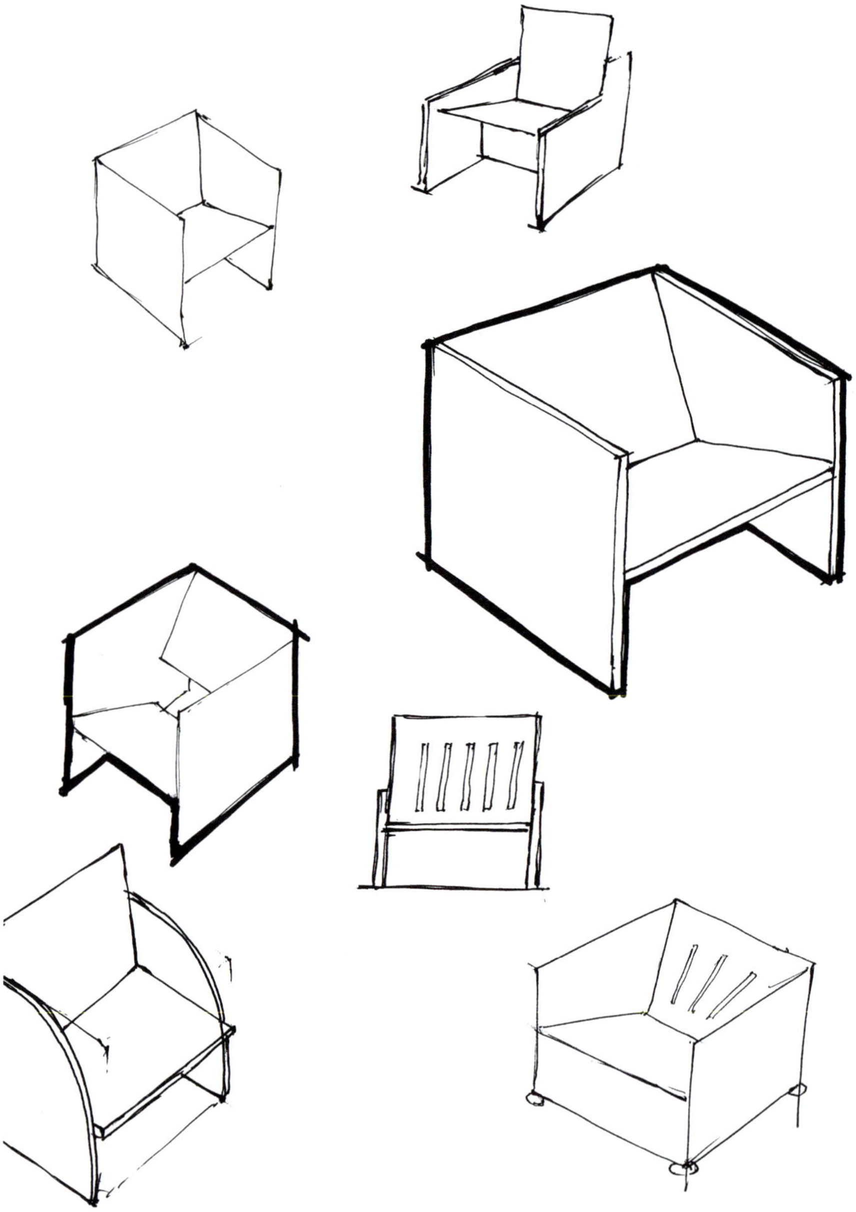

Figure 42 Chair sketches made with cheap fine-point pens

The sketches of the chairs shown in Figure 42 offer a more lifelike appearance. These are drawn in *perspective*. They are the sort of views we might get if we took photographs of the 3D model. But they do contain distortions.

Look at the large central image in Figure 42. Use a ruler to measure the height of the front edge of one side in the perspective sketch and compare it with the height of the back edge of the same side – the back edge is smaller than the front edge. The drawing is attempting to simulate a visual illusion that continually takes place all around us – that is, objects appear to recede in size the further they are away from us. This is the illusion of 'foreshortening'.

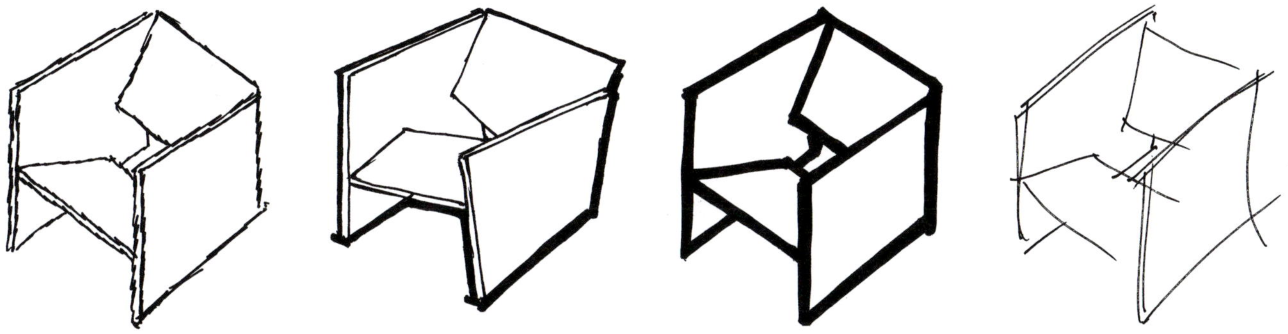

(a) Woolly or scribbled lines **(b) Perspective inconsistent or components disjointed** **(c) Lines too heavy** **(d) Rushed drawing**

Figure 43 Some basic errors in line drawings

The drawings shown in Figure 42 possess a number of qualities. One of these qualities is the quality of perspective. I'm going to deal with this in Sections 6 and 7 so I'll say no more about this just yet. Another important quality is the quality of the line work. Figure 43 illustrates this point. Here are four sketches of the same chair but this time I have deliberately introduced some basic errors into the line work. Try to avoid these common mistakes but, at the same time, I encourage you to develop your own personal style of sketching.

4.6 Using overlays to create sketches

One simple way to create or recreate sketches is to use a sheet of paper which is sufficiently transparent to place over an existing drawing or photo and then to copy the image with a pencil or pen. Tracing paper and layout paper can be used (examples of both are included in the T211 *Paper pack*). You can either copy the image underneath exactly or you can adapt and change it as desired. A lot of designers use this technique because an earlier drawing or sketch (or even a photo of a rough model) can be used to assist in developing the design in the next sketch. Any parts of the design which are to be retained are redrawn as before while any modifications are simple to add. Overlays can save a lot of time and effort in developing a design.

Activity 8 gives you some practice with using overlays to create some simple perspective drawings of your own.

Activity 8 Using overlays

Toolkit

An inexpensive fine-point ink pen (or a ball-point if necessary)

Two A4 sheets of tracing paper or layout paper (from the *Paper pack*)

Take one A4 sheet of tracing paper or layout paper from the *Paper pack* and place it over the large central image of the chair in Figure 42. To hold it in place you can either use a couple of paper clips, adhesive tape or simply use your free hand but it's important that the paper doesn't move as you copy. Using a fine-point ink pen (or ball-point pen if necessary) copy the image. Aim to create straight clean lines and sharp corners. Try to avoid the mistakes shown in Figure 43.

Use the perspective drawing you've just copied in an overlay for new ideas for flat-pack chairs. Simply place a new sheet of tracing or layout paper over your sketch and instead of copying the sketch exactly, try modifying some of the shapes to produce new chair ideas. The drawing underneath guides your new lines leaving you free to be creative.

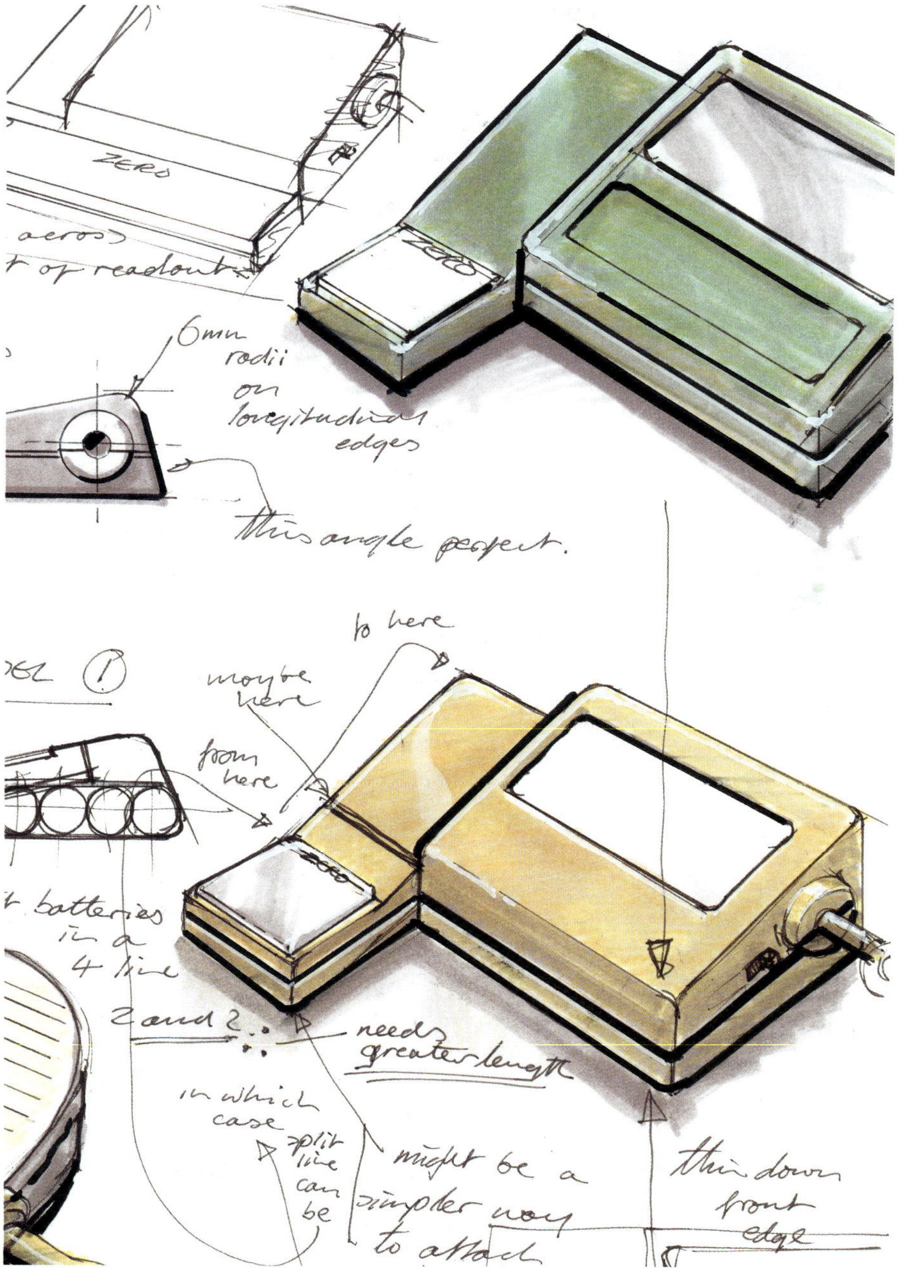

If you look closely at Figure 44 you'll see that some of the sketches in this design exploit the overlay technique. Some are perspective views and some are orthographic views

Figure 44 Detail from sketches of a personal weighing scale

These sketches show the use of overlays to assist in the rapid generation of drawings that display variations.

5 Orthographic projection

5.1 Views of reality

The term 'orthographic' refers to the angle of projection between the object depicted and the individual image of it. Basically, it means 'drawn straight-on'. In Section 4 you produced three orthographic sketches of the cardboard chair model – the front, the side and the plan and you produced a perspective sketch using the overlay technique.

Both systems of drawing can be categorised as attempts to visualise three-dimensional 'reality' on two-dimensional paper. Both involve, and to some extent rely on, distortions so that the illusion is relatively convincing. The root of the distortions lies in the attempt to capture information about the three-dimensional form in one picture plane. Orthographic projection gets around this by assembling several different picture planes into one larger picture plane. I'll use the dice from Section 2 to illustrate the principle, then move on to some more complex images to discuss the uses of orthographic projection.

Figure 45

Figure 46

Figure 45 shows a perspective drawing of a dice. We can see that the top face shows a '6', the right hand face shows a '2' and the left hand face shows a '3'. An orthographic drawing would treat the faces as three separate but related images. If you had the dice in front of you, you could rotate it in your hand to see the three separate views as you did with the chair model. You could then simply present the three images in order (as in Figure 46) but there are conventions that help people to exploit and 'read' orthographic drawings.

The conventions state precisely how views are laid out. Their location indicates the relationship of one view to those around it. In Figure 47 the top face (6) is presented above the '3', and the '2' is presented to the right of '3' as they are in the perspective sketch. There are two important points to note. Firstly, this drawing convention permits us to include more information than can be shown with one perspective drawing (Figure 47 also shows the faces '1', '4' and '5' in their respective locations – face '4' could appear on either the far right or far left side). Secondly, all the faces of the dice are presented distortion-free. Each appears as a true square.

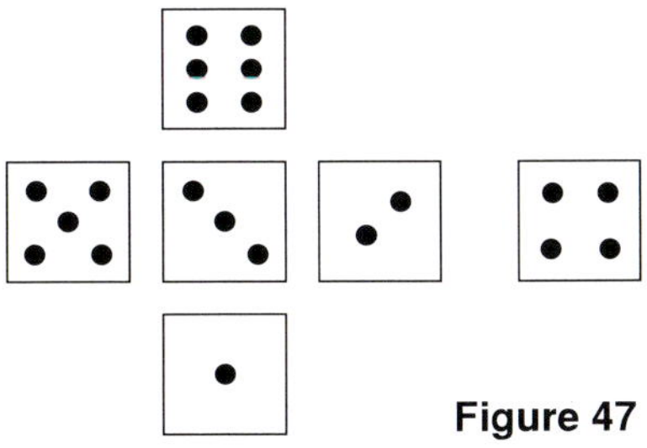

Figure 47

It was a variation of this convention you were following when you laid out your three orthographic views of your chair model.

This is a far more accurate representation of reality than a perspective drawing. In fact, it's so accurate, if you join the faces together to make a 'net' of all the faces you could cut out the shape, assemble it and make yourself a cardboard dice! (Figure 48) You couldn't do that with a perspective drawing!

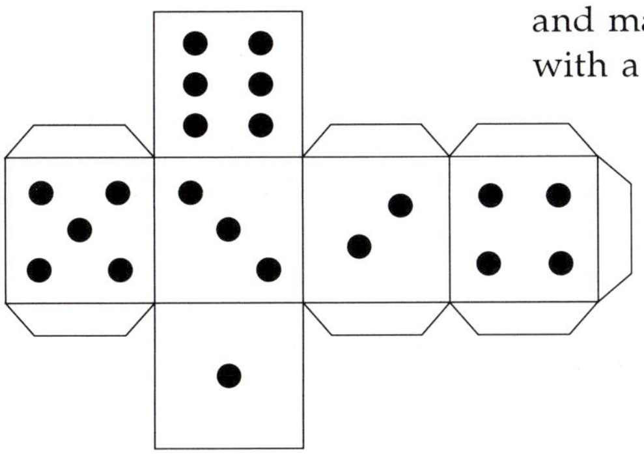

Figure 48 A 'net' of a dice (with tabs added to enable it to be cut out and assembled into an accurate three-dimensional cube)

There are two conventions used for laying out the various views created by orthographic projection. The one shown above is *third-angle projection*. The alternative, the one you used for the drawing of your chair, is *first-angle projection*. I'll move to a different orthographic drawing to explain this.

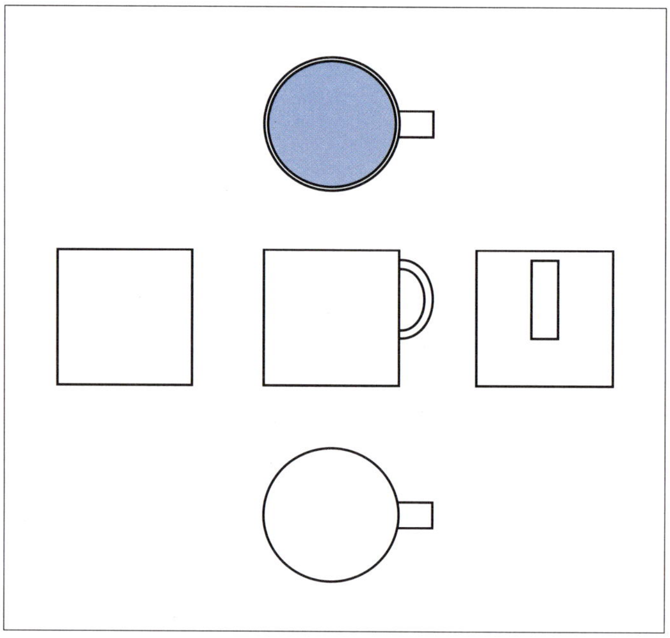

(a) Mug drawn in orthographic 'third angle'

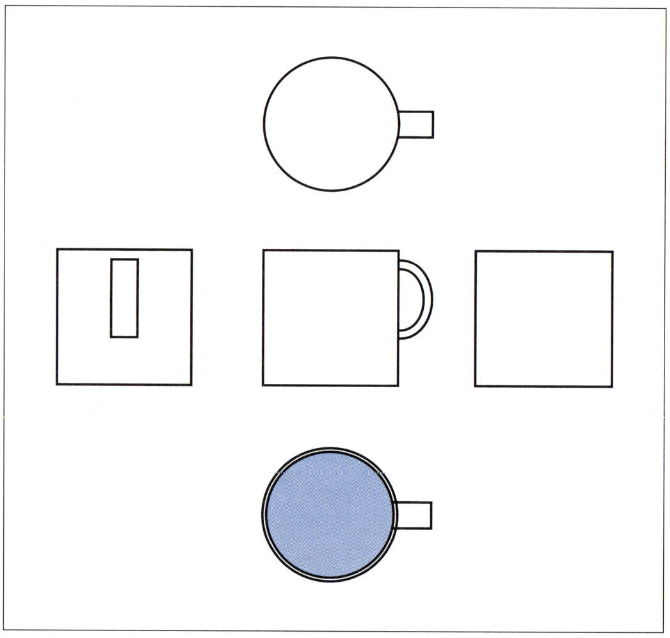

(b) Mug drawn in orthographic 'first angle'

Figure 49

Figure 49 shows my coffee mug that I used in Activity 6. The blue circle represents the coffee in the mug. Figure 49(a) is drawn in third-angle projection just like the dice above. Each image is placed next to the face it represents. Figure 49(b) is drawn in first-angle projection. Each image is placed on the opposite side to the face it represents. These views are the ones you would get if you looked 'through' the object from the far side of the central image. Your sketch of the chair in Activity 7 was drawn in first-angle projection.

Activity 9 Sketching orthographic views

Toolkit

Ball-point pen or fine-point pen

Two A4 sheets of squared paper

Ruler

Two objects as directed

This activity involves sketching the front view, the side view and the plan view of an object of yours in first-angle orthographic projection. You will need a simple product that is not too complicated in its outer form. Avoid using basic boxes because the views of the faces might be very similar. I suggest using a decorative but simple object that mostly has flat sides (we'll deal with complex curved forms later). Use a fine-point or ball-point pen for this activity.

1 Measure the length, height and width of your object and decide what scale you will make your drawing so that it will fit onto an A4 sheet of paper.

2 Using a sheet of squared A4 paper draw three rectangles to your chosen scale. These will be the front view, the side view and the plan view in first-angle orthographic projection. Take care to get each rectangle to line up with those around it.

3 Measure the parts of the object, convert these to scaled dimensions and sketch these inside your rectangles. If you follow lines horizontally and vertically the details on one view will help you find the same details on other views. There's no need to show hidden detail.

   This is the sort of preparatory sketch one might make before laying out an orthographic drawing properly. You can see my attempt in Figure 50.

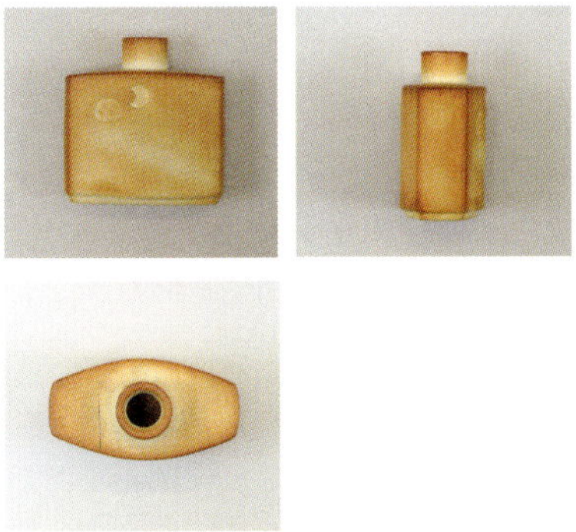

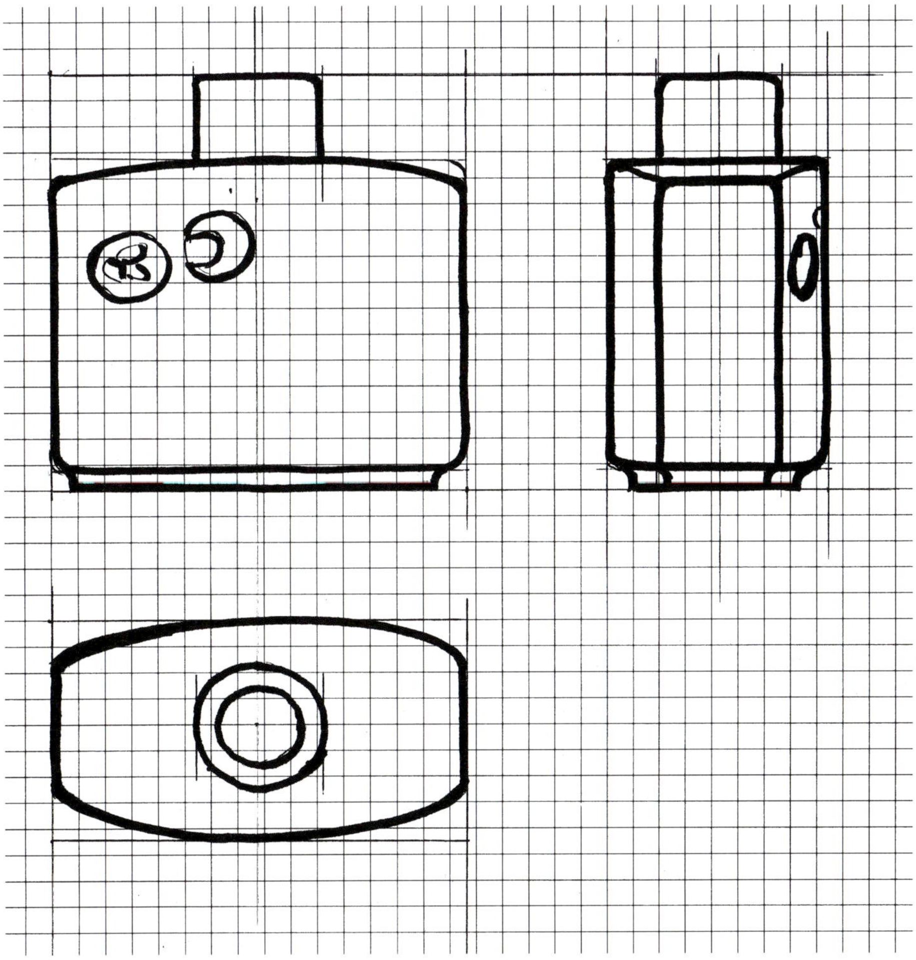

Figure 50 Orthographic sketches of a ceramic vase

4 Using a more complex object – I've used a child's toy tractor – use the same techniques to produce a sketch of the front view, back view, one side view and plan view in third-angle orthographic projection (Figure 51).

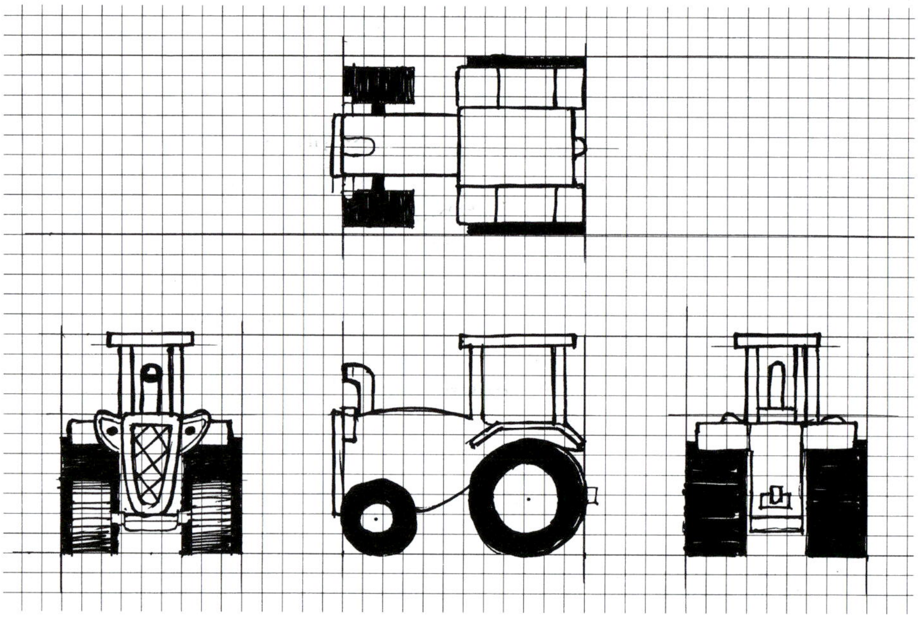

Figure 51 Orthographic views of the toy tractor

5.2 Sections

Both first-angle and third-angle conventions allow for the inclusion of *sections* in drawings. A section is a slice through the object and is drawn to reveal internal information or changes in profile where shapes are complex. Various professions have developed their own conventions for sections to reflect their particular requirements. On a simple level:

- where a section cuts through solid material this is represented in the drawing by cross-hatched lines;
- where a section cuts through voids or spaces these are left blank, that is without cross-hatched lines;
- where two different parts appear next to each other they are distinguished by differences in the cross-hatching style.

Sections through some common objects are depicted in Figure 52. Note how this drawing convention is used to convey information not apparent in the other views.

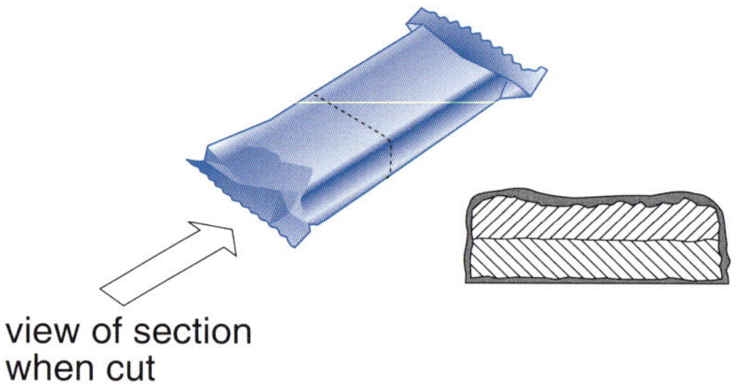

(a) Section through a confectionary bar (caramel upper portion, biscuit base below)

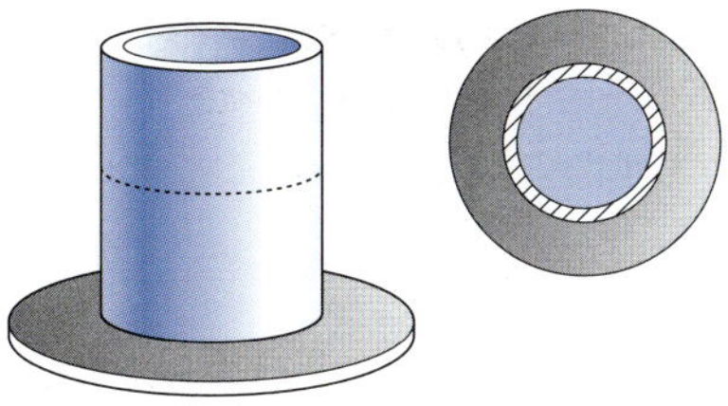

(b) Section through a ceramic vase

Figure 52

A section will not only include those parts being cut by the particular section line chosen. It will also include the outlines of those parts lying beyond the section line. For example, look at the ceramic vase in Figure 53. We see the cut cylinder; we also see the outline of the base below it.

The communication of sections is a rather abstract convention. The cross-hatching doesn't exist in reality – it is helpful because it shows where material is cut and where there is a void or space. In some contexts, notably in building, there are further conventions determining the precise meaning of the colours used or the cross-hatching style used in drawings. The use of different styles of cross-hatching also works to differentiate between the cutting of one component and the cutting of another. In fact a section line might pass through several components. Sections allow designers to communicate detail design. The information presented in sections allows people to determine, for example, strengths of components or costs.

Activity 10 Bracket sections

Toolkit

Any pencil

An A4 sheet of plain paper

Eraser

This activity aims to increase your ability to understand and generate sections. Figure 53 shows a rather ordinary metal shelf bracket. It's the sort of thing you might find in a hardware shop or DIY store. It's made from steel, pressed into a right angle, and strengthened with a welded steel triangular insert. There are two holes in the top and two in the front so it can be screwed to walls and shelves.

Figure 53

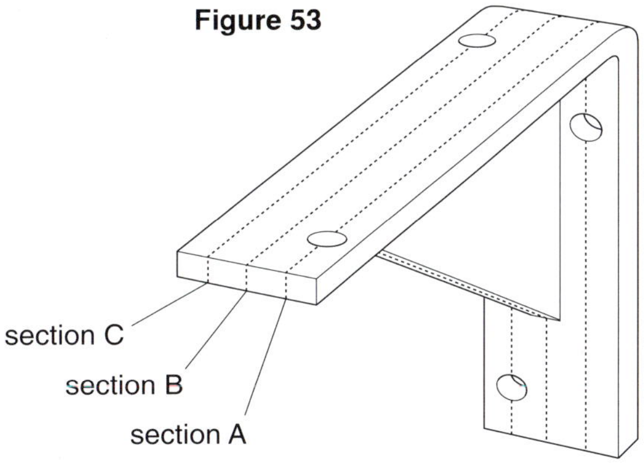

I have drawn onto this bracket three lines labelled as section A, section B and section C. If you were to cut this bracket along these three section lines you would get three different sections.

Your task is to draw a bracket underneath each of the 3 shelves shown in Figure 54 that corresponds to each section line (viewed from the right). Include the holes if they are cut by a section line but you don't need to show any screws. Use hatching to show where the material has been cut.

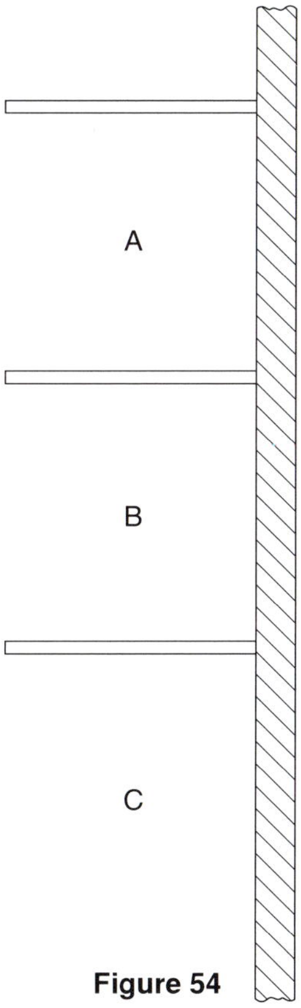

Figure 54

The solution appears on the next page (Figure 55).

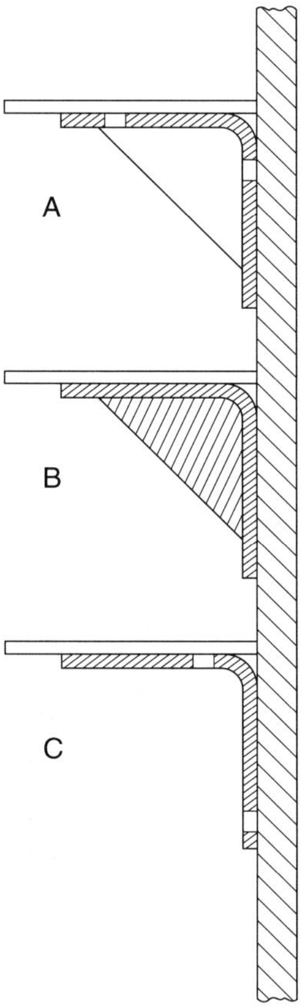

Figure 55

In Section B the triangular insert is cut along its length so I have shown this cross-hatched but in a different direction to the main bracket. However, strictly speaking, drawing conventions state that thin inserts such as this are rarely shown cross-hatched.

In professional practice orthographic drawings can become very complex (see Figure 56). They can become difficult to read and, when drawn by hand, they were often difficult to change.

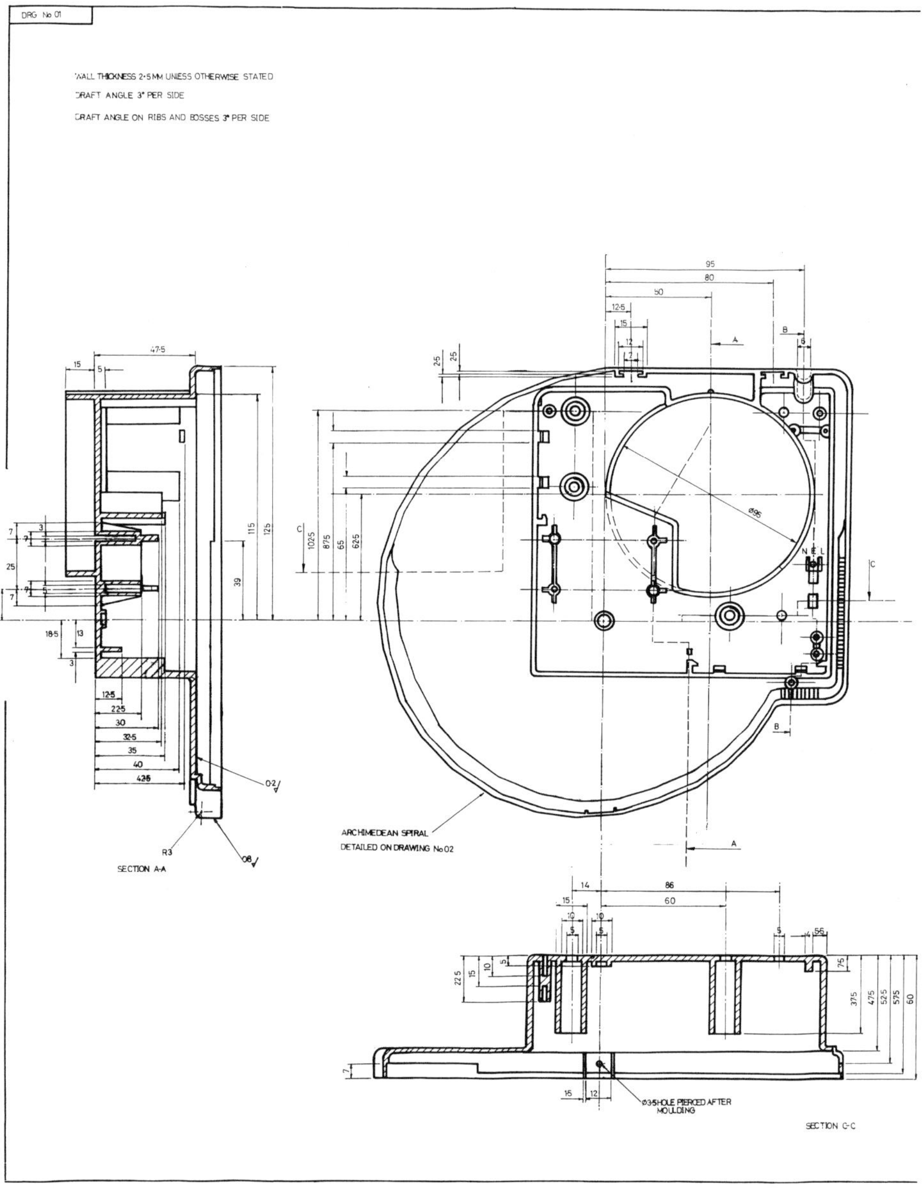

Figure 56 Example of a complex orthographic projection drawing for a wall fan

Most complex orthographic drawings are now constructed on computer where they can be easily made and amended in stages; they can also be integrated with other digital modelling for presentation or analysis. Another benefit of using a computer-based drawing package is that drawings can be easily exchanged over computer networks.

The principles of orthographic projection are not limited to the construction of such complex drawings. Designers also use the principles of orthographic drawing in their design sketches. Figure 57 shows a sketch for a public information point conveyed in front and side elevation. Figure 58 is from the same project and shows a sketched section through an assembly of components. Both are extensively annotated to convey further information.

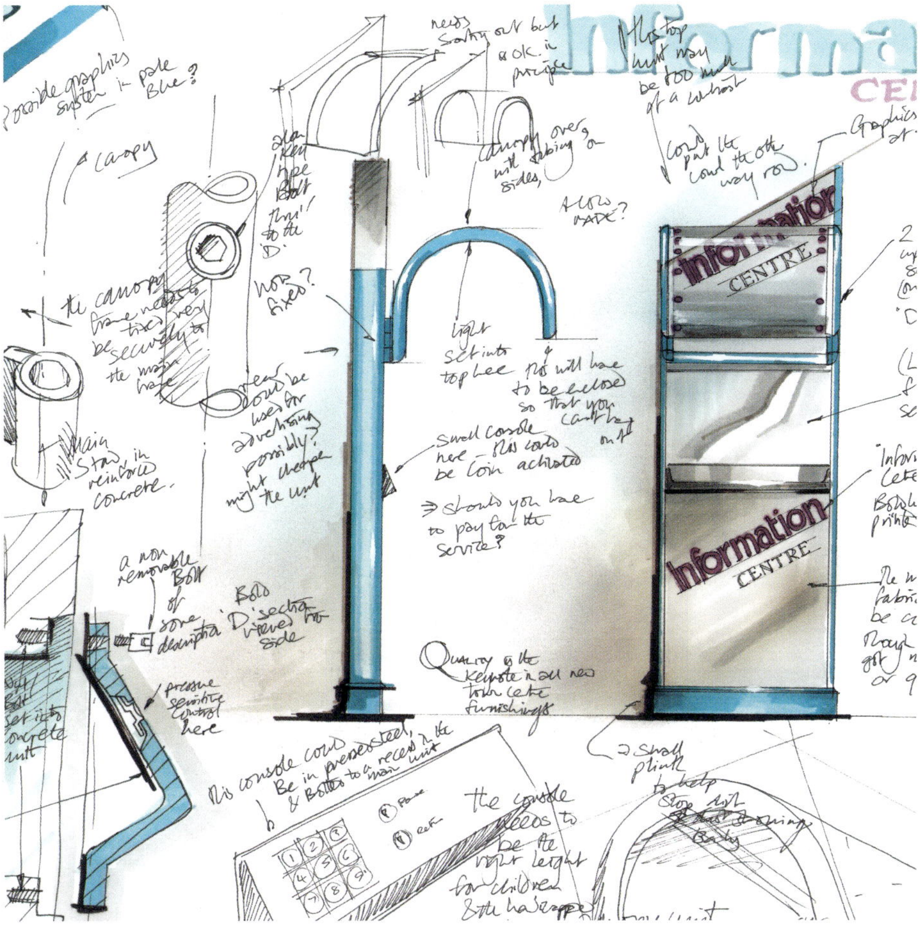

Figure 57 A concept sketch for a public information point

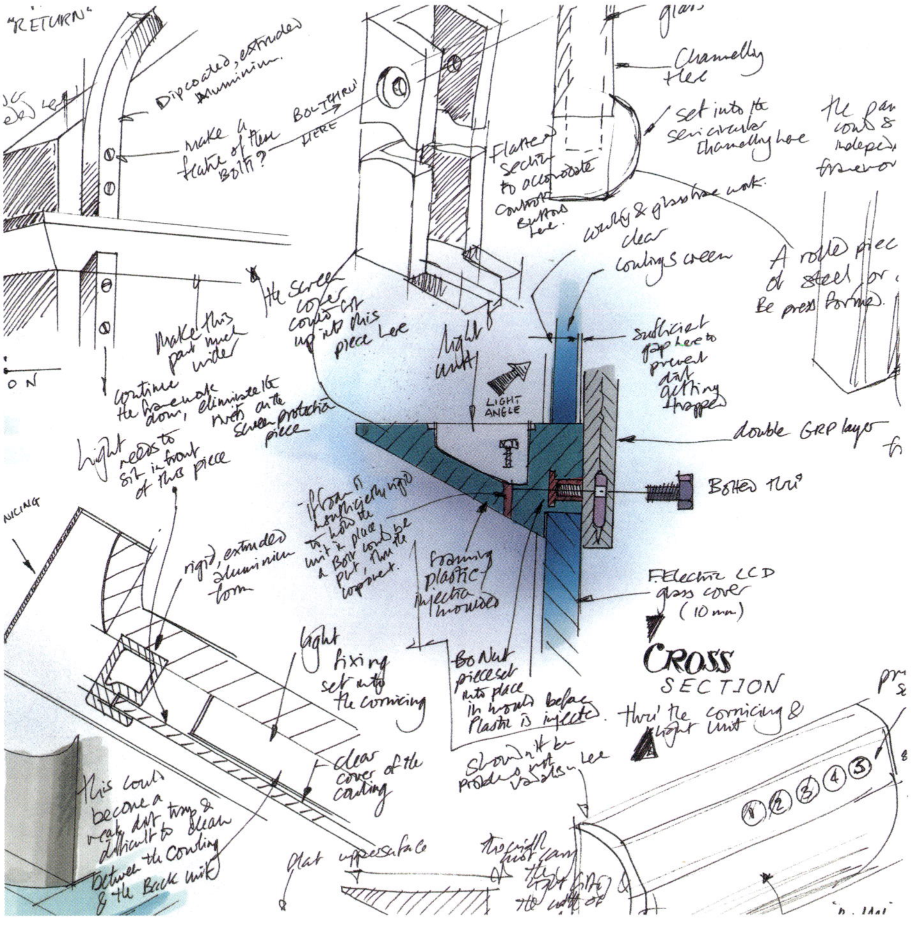

Figure 58 A sketched section through an assembly of components

6 Perspective drawing

6.1 Vanishing points

In Section 4 you made sketches of your chair model. The orthographic sketches presented 'straight-on' views of the front, the side and the plan. When you used the overlay technique you copied a perspective view. Each of these drawing conventions has their own advantages and disadvantages and a designer needs to be competent with both drawing systems. As I've already noted, in perspective drawing the angles and dimensions are distorted to different extents in different parts of the drawing so it's impossible to take any accurate measurements from it. A perspective drawing is of limited use to someone who has to actually make the object depicted but it probably gives the most realistic and natural-seeming views. A knowledge of perspective will improve your sketching ability and assist you to present clear and life-like images in your design work. Let's start with a simple perspective drawing.

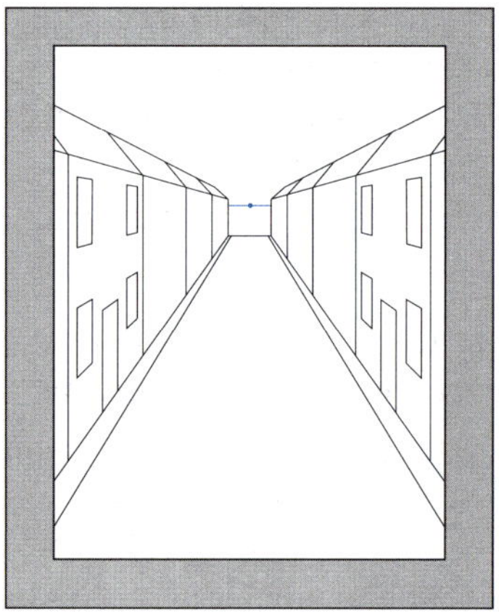

Figure 59

Consider the image shown in Figure 59. It depicts a view out of an upstairs window of a building. We see the window frame and through this we see a street where the lines of the houses seem to converge at a point on the horizon in the far distance.

This is an example of 'single-point' perspective. The lines converge at a single *vanishing point*. We judge the houses on each side of the street to be equal in height and width but they are drawn progressively smaller as they get closer to the vanishing point. This is the phenomenon of *foreshortening* introduced in Section 4. Single-point perspective is not a particularly important drawing convention. It does however allow me to introduce some of the principles of perspective that will be discussed in this section.

Figure 60

We have three things here:

- the viewer, and more particularly their eye point or *viewpoint*;
- the view: the world outside the window including the various buildings, cars, people etc;
- the window between the viewer and the view. This is also known as the *picture plane*.

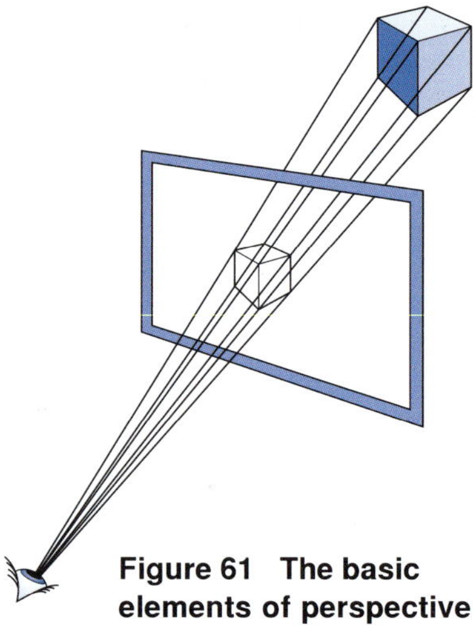

Figure 61 The basic elements of perspective projection

If you stood near to a window and kept your head still you might be able to draw onto the glass an image of the view. It wouldn't take much skill because you would be simply tracing around the shapes that you could see (a bit like using the overlay technique). However, you'd probably create a passable representation of the scene on your window or picture plane. Viewpoints, vanishing points and the creation of images on a picture plane are central to this section of the workbook.

Let us now consider the drawing of an object rather than a view of a landscape. I'll use the dice again to illustrate this. A perspective view of the dice is shown in Figure 60.

Figure 61 shows the elements that were needed to make this drawing. There is the eye of the viewer, an object (in this case the dice), and between these is a picture plane (perhaps a sheet of glass or other transparent material).

If you were the viewer looking, with one eye only, at the dice through the picture plane you could easily mark on the picture plane all the corners you could see. You could then take this picture plane and join up the dots with straight lines to achieve a reasonably accurate image of the cube as you saw it. If you had also marked on the picture plane all the spots you could see on the faces of the dice you would have an even more life-like representation.

> You need to be looking through the picture plane using only one eye because with binocular vision – the use of two eyes that are slightly spaced apart – your brain would automatically use the information from both eyes to improve your perception of real three-dimensional space.

I've already highlighted one negative feature of making perspective drawings – you cannot take any measurements from the image on the picture plane. On the positive side it produces line drawings that closely match our views of objects in the world around us. It's a technique that has been known to artists since the Renaissance. It can be used to draw an image of small objects such as the dice and the technique can also be used to create images of large objects such as buildings. To do this the object under study needs to be further from the picture plane. I can easily demonstrate this. Put your hands together as shown in Figure 62, creating a 'window' or picture plane with your fingers.

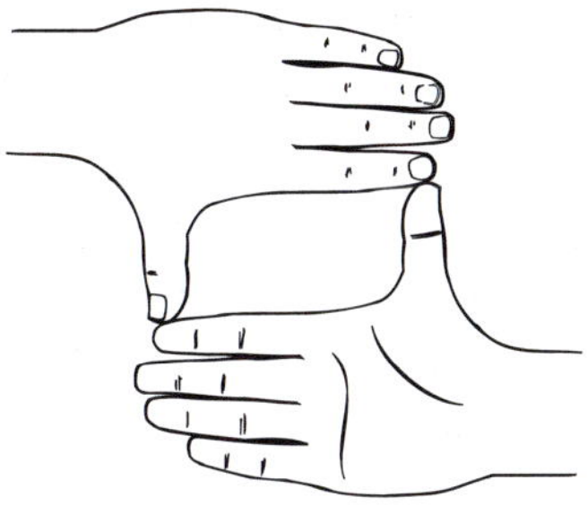

Figure 62

Look through your finger window at something small but close to you such as a book or coffee cup. Now move your finger window so that you can look at something farther away – perhaps a car outside your house or a piece of furniture in another room. You can make a large object fit your picture plane by having the picture plane nearer you and further from the object being studied.

As objects are moved further from the viewpoint, their image in any given picture plane become smaller due to foreshortening. But this is not the only type of distortion taking place. As you can see in Figure 60, the square sides of the dice do not appear as squares in the image. They are distorted and it's this distortion, when presented consistently, which we interpret as three-dimensionality. If I represent the scene shown in Figure 61 again, but this time as our imaginary viewer is looking at it you will see that the distortions are consistent. The lines representing the edges of the cube converge towards two *vanishing points* (Figure 63).

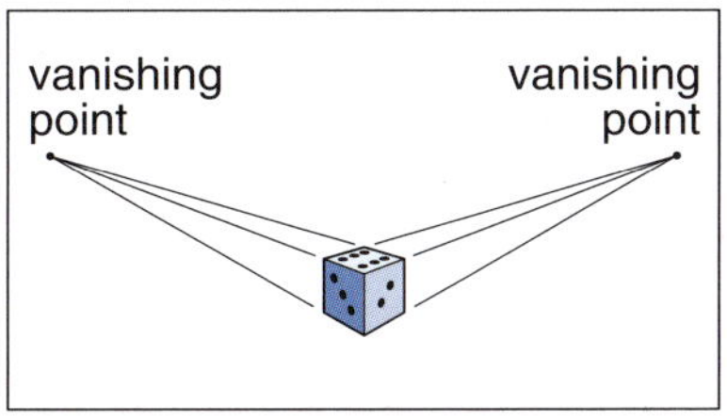

Figure 63

Fortunately, the principles of perspective allow us to create representations of three-dimensional forms without setting up a picture plane in front of a real object.

Let's move to a few drawing activities.

Activity 11 Box in two-point perspective

Toolkit

An A3 sheet of plain paper (or two sheets of A4 taped side by side)

B or 2B pencil

Eraser

Ruler

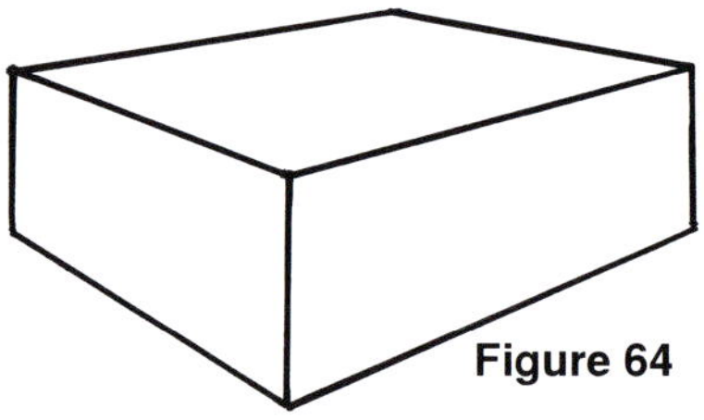

Figure 64

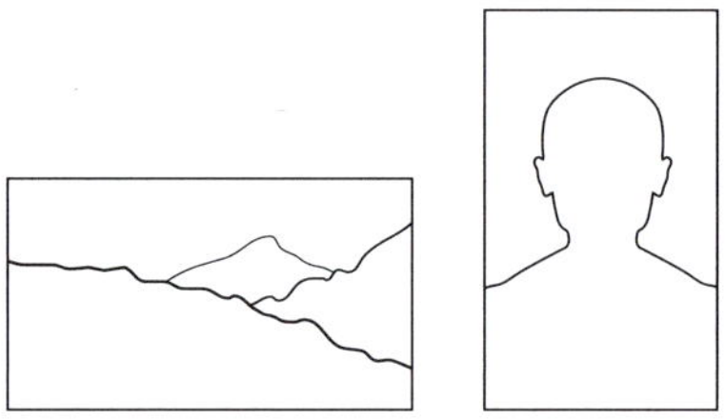

Figure 65 Landscape and portrait page formats

Part of the skill of creating images in perspective is setting up appropriate vanishing points. For this activity I'm going to give you the dimensions necessary to create two vanishing points plus the front edge of the object. The drawing also requires you to make some estimations of your own! The first perspective image you will construct will be of a low rectilinear box. It doesn't matter about the exact proportions. In later activities the proportions will matter! Figure 64 shows the box I will draw.

1 Turn your A3 size plain paper so that it is in 'landscape' format (see Figure 65) and draw two horizontal lines using a ruler or straight edge. Make one about 25 mm from the top of the paper and a second line exactly 100 mm below the first. Mark the top one 'horizon line' and the lower one 'object line'.

2 On the horizon line mark two vanishing points each 20 mm in from the left and right hand edges. Call these VP1 and VP2 as shown below.

3 Draw a vertical line 180 mm from the left-hand side of the paper. This will be the 'front edge' of the object to be drawn. I'll call the junction of this front edge line and the object line the 'object point'.

4 Now you can begin to join up some of the points we have created using feint 'construction' lines. Join the object point to VP1 and VP2. These will indicate the bottom front edges of your box.

5 The front edge line is the only place where you can introduce vertical measurements. I'm going to make the height of my box in this drawing 40 mm. You can either use 40 mm as well or pick a height between 20–50 mm and mark this vertically from the object point. Now join this new point to VP1 and VP2 giving you the top front edges of your box.

6 Since this is an imaginary box you can decide where to put the left-hand and right-hand vertical edges. I suggest you don't place them too far away from the object point or your box will look very distorted. The left and right edges need to be vertical so use the front edge line or the edges of your paper as a guide to getting these lines vertical. Now join your back corners to VP1 and VP2. Finally go over the outlines of the box again so they stand out and the box is clear. You may also rub out any of your feint guide lines if you wish.

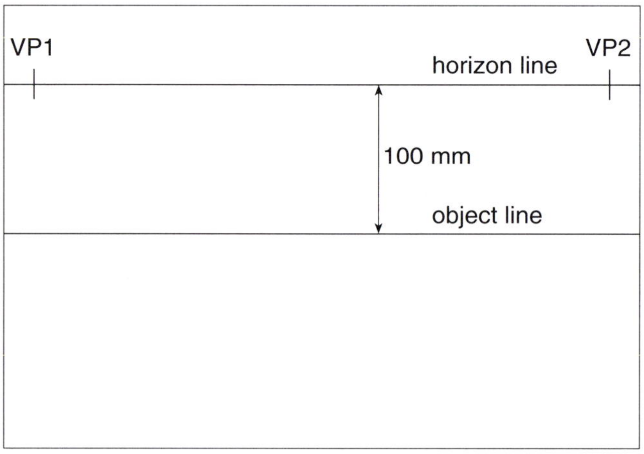

(a) Stages 1 and 2

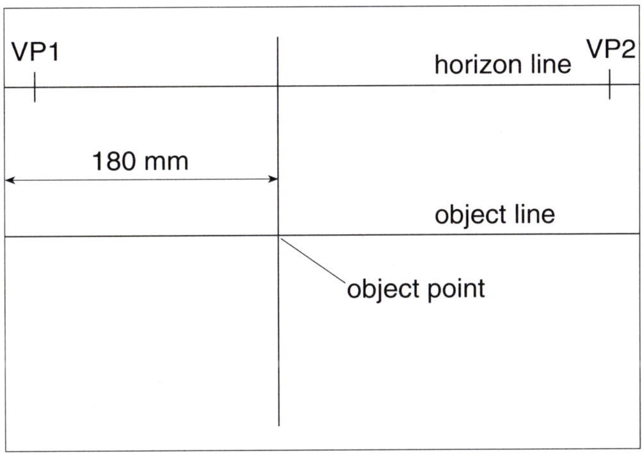

(b) Stage 3

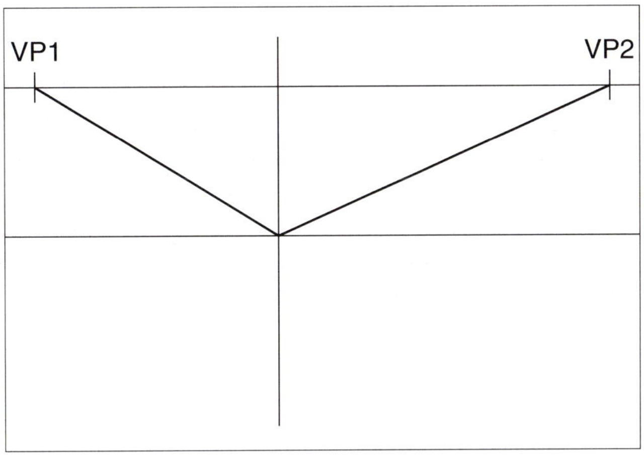

(c) Stage 4

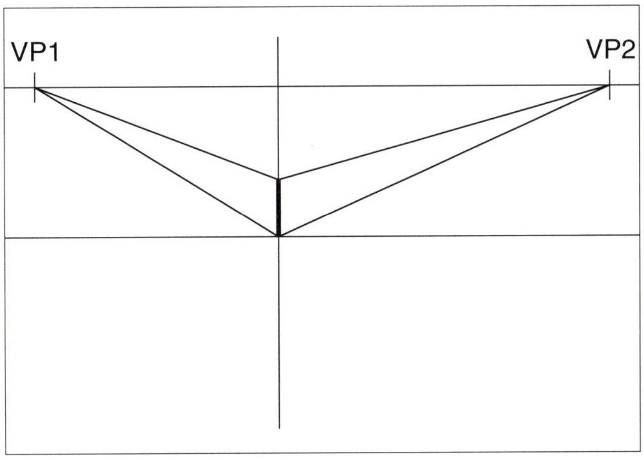

(d) Stage 5

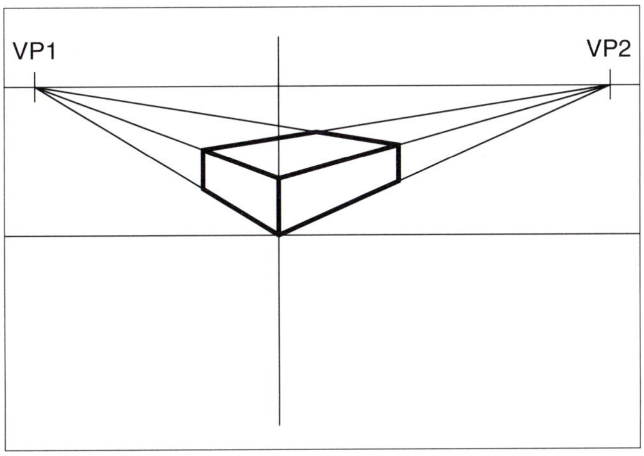

(e) Stage 6

Figure 66

Activity 12 Upright box

Toolkit

An A3 sheet of plain paper (or two sheets of A4 taped side by side)

B or 2B pencil

Eraser

Ruler

Using exactly the same planning grid as in Activity 11 your task is to construct a perspective line drawing of another box. This time the image should look like a cardboard cereal packet – that is, it should be tall and broad but relatively thin. To assist you in your judgements a few packets of differing proportions are shown in the photograph (Figure 67).

Figure 67 A selection of breakfast cereal packets

1. Follow instructions 1 to 4 in Activity 11 but this time make your horizon line 75 mm from the top of the paper. Then continue with instruction 2 below.
2. Make your front edge 130 mm tall (that is, measure up 130 mm from the object point). You'll see that this takes it just above the horizon line! Join the ends of this front edge to VP1 and VP2.
3. Next you'll need to estimate the depth and breadth of the box you want to portray. Do this simply by judgement. Try to make it look like the box on the left in Figure 67. Add the left and right-hand edges taking care to draw them as vertical lines.
4. Go over the outline of your box. Add some graphic detail.

Figure 68 Perspective drawing of a cereal packet

Design sketching sometimes requires that we follow drawing rules and conventions (such as establishing vanishing points); at other times our visual judgements are more important. Often, we need to use rules and judgements together. I'll illustrate this.

6.2 Suggesting scale with perspective

I'm going to present you with three line drawings. All three seek to communicate the three dimensional form of cubes and they all achieve this illusion solely by the use of perspective. However, all three cubes look different (Figure 69).

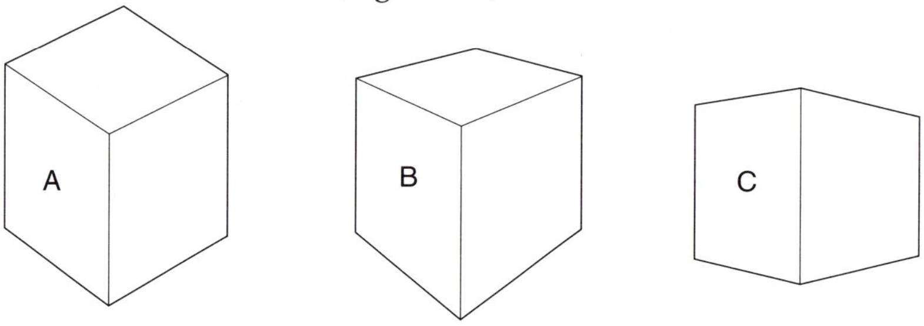

Figure 69 Cubes A, B and C

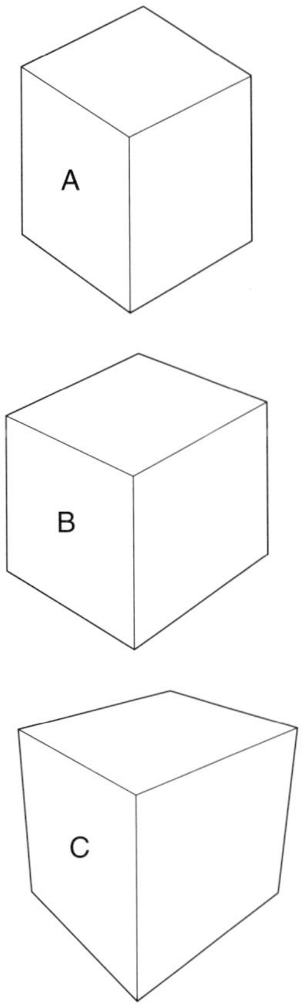

Figure 70 Cubes A, B and C

These three cubes are the starting point for three different drawings that I will complete to:

1 depict a new model of a washing machine (a cube whose sides measure 600 mm);
2 become my proposal for a new building (a cube whose sides measure 6 m); and
3 represent a cardboard box for a small perfume bottle (a cube whose sides measure 60 mm).

Which cube would best suit each purpose?

I suggest the following is logical:

1 cube B will become the washing machine drawing;
2 cube C will become the architectural proposal;
3 cube A will become the illustration of the perfume bottle packaging.

'Ah,' you think, 'the clue is in what can be seen of the top surface'. Where we can clearly see the top, that is, where we appear to be looking down on the cube we assume it is a small object. Where we cannot see the top we assume we are smaller than the object. That is a reasonable explanation. Just like in Activity 12 I have constructed cube C so that it straddles the imaginary horizon line and therefore it appears to tower above the viewer. In Activity 12 we used this technique not to represent a building but to produce a very dramatic-looking cereal packet! Cube B seems to suggest that it is slightly smaller than ourselves because it lies just below the horizon line. Of the three objects cube A is the only one where we get a strong sense of looking down onto it.

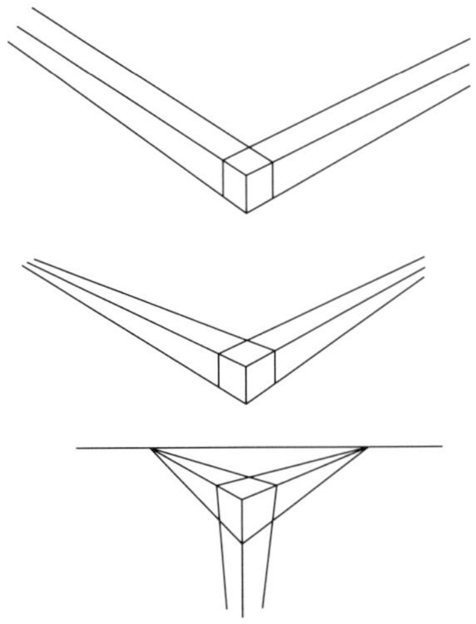

Figure 71 Cubes A, B and C with perspective lines

Let me present these three cubes again, in the same order, but this time in a less dramatic way. We can see the top of each cube equally but we are still able to perceive differences in the scale of the cubes (Figure 70).

The differences here have been created solely via my estimated positioning of the horizon line and the vanishing points (Figure 71).

For cube C (the architectural scale object) the horizon line would be only a short distance above the cube and the vanishing points will be quite close together and close to the object point. Cube C is further distorted because I have added a slight tapering to the uprights (a third vanishing point some way below the object).

For Cube A (the very small object) the horizon line is a long way above the cube and the vanishing points are spread far apart.

Cube B is somewhere between these two extremes.

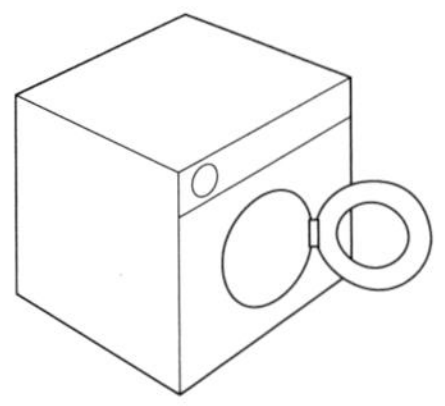

Figure 72 Washing machine 'cube'

As the maker of drawings we have a lot of control over what scale people 'read' into them. When we add detail to our basic outlines the illusion of scale is further enhanced (Figure 72).

Alternatively, we might choose to deliberately use some of these techniques to achieve a dramatic effect. For example, drawing a small object as if it is a piece of architecture by bringing the vanishing points close to the object (as we did with the cereal packet in Activity 12) or drawing a building with very little perspective, thus making it appear as if it were a child's toy. As designers, we can improve our communication if we exploit our knowledge of such drawing techniques.

Let's now turn to some basic sketching skills that will help you to apply this knowledge of perspective construction.

6.3 Sketching in perspective

If every sketch we ever made depended on us laboriously setting out vanishing points we would quickly tire of using drawing at all. Sketching sometimes needs to be rapid – especially where it seeks to convey thought which is itself developing and changing. Next I offer a number of sketching activities that seek to combine a fast and confident sketching style with some knowledge of perspective.

Activity 13 Quick perspective cube

Toolkit

An A4 sheet of plain paper

B or 2B pencil

Eraser

A4 tracing paper and/or A4 layout paper (optional)

1. Using any plain paper, A4 size is quite adequate, and a relatively soft (B or 2B) pencil, draw freehand a 'Y' shape as in Figure 73(a). Make each arm approximately 50 mm in length.
2. Sketch lines above and below the right-hand arm. Make sure they are both slightly angled in towards the extremities of the drawing to give the impression of perspective (that is, converging on an estimated vanishing point). It doesn't matter if they are over-long or if they won't exactly meet at a vanishing point.
3. Repeat for the left-hand arm. Then draw vertical lines down from the ends of both arms to complete the cube.
4. Give you box a bold outline and erase the guide lines if necessary.

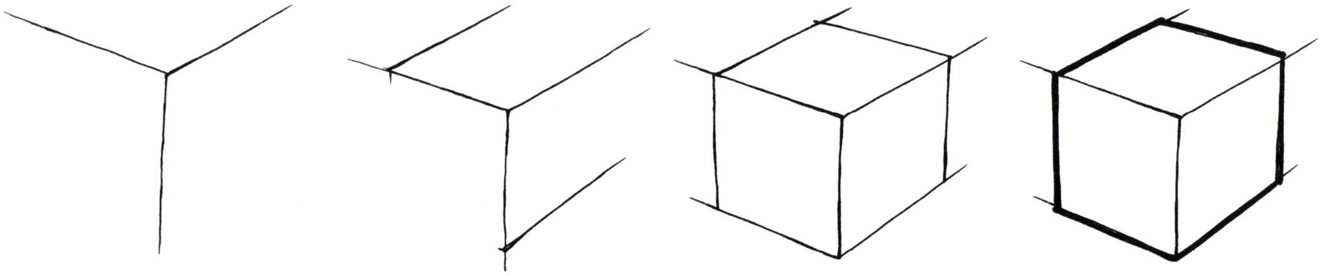

(a) Stages 1-4

This activity requires you to make judgements when drawing your lines. If you have difficulties, try using the overlay technique described in Activity 8 to build up your familiarity with the lines and shapes of these cubes. Use tracing paper or layout paper to make sketch copies of some of the cubes shown in these pages or those in Section 2.4.

If you are not using overlays it's always best to begin a drawing of a cube with the 'Y' shape in the centre. If this is easy for you try modifying the angles of the arms of the Y so that you can suggest the cube is turned slightly as in Figure 73(b).

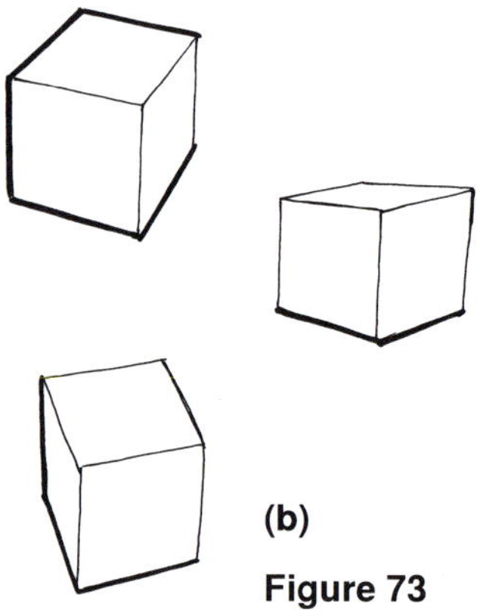

(b)

Figure 73

Activity 14 Double cubes

Toolkit

Two A4 sheets of plain paper

B or 2B pencil

Eraser

Rule

You can do this activity entirely freehand or use a ruler or straight edge if you find this helps.

1 Using the 'Y' technique shown in Activity 13 sketch a cube. We are going to convert this into a double cube (Figure 74).

2 Extend the front edge vertically upwards so that the front edge is doubled in height. Add two new arms at the top of this line which conform to the perspective established by the lower arms. Again an estimation is all that is required.

3 Extend the remaining two verticals upwards to meet the left and right arms.

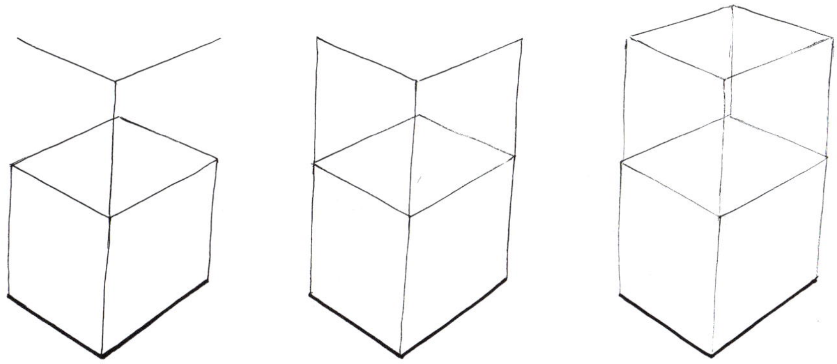

Figure 74 (a) Creating a vertical double cube

4 Add the top rear edges as you did when constructing the single cube. Put this drawing to one side. We will use it again later.

5 On another sheet of paper sketch a single cube as before and extend one edge. I have brought the left upper arm forward (Figure 74(b), stage 5).

6 Extend the other edges forward. It doesn't matter if you make them too long initially. Now make a judgement about where the end face should be. The front cube will have edges that are slightly longer than the ones on the back cube due to foreshortening. Sketch the end face at this point.

7 Erase the guide lines and the now hidden lines of the first cube. Save this drawing for use later.

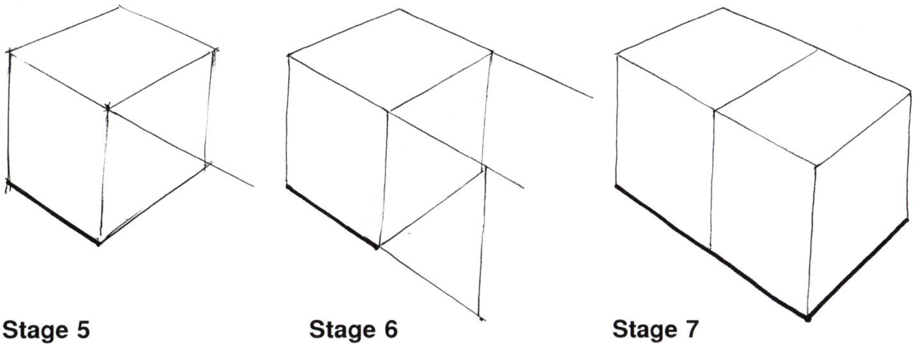

Figure 74 (b) Creating a side-by-side double cube

If you had difficulty estimating the foreshortening try the following technique. It is founded on our knowledge of the principles of squares.

Draw two squares of any size, one on top of the other. Project the diagonal of the top one to the base line.

This creates the front point of a third square from which the vertical and then the horizontal lines can be added (Figure 75, stage 2). I can use this same principle to assist my depiction of cubes drawn in perspective.

Using a sketch of a cube, project a rear edge upwards of the same dimension as that edge. Next project the base line forward. Connect the top of the rear line with the front corner of the cube and continue it down to the base line.

Where the diagonal meets the base line strike a vertical line. Then project forward the edges of the rear cube. Finally estimate the perspective on the right hand face and sketch the final two lines to complete the second cube (since your original cube is estimated you may get distortion in the front cube).

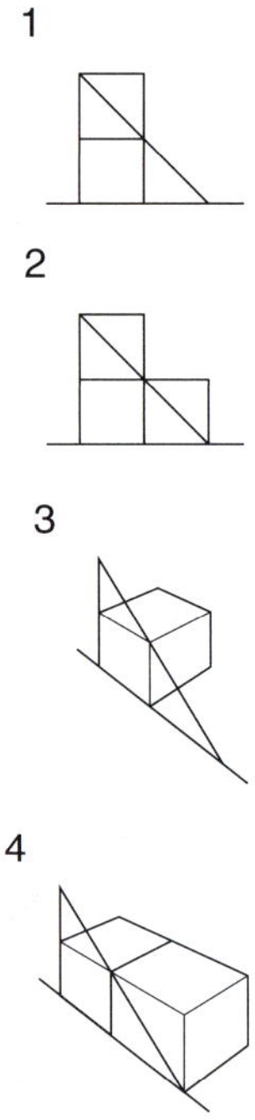

Figure 75
Guidelines for constructing squares and cubes

Activity 15 Crating

Toolkit

Drawings (or copies) from Activity 14

A4 layout paper

Ball-point or fine-point pen

This activity will require you to sketch into and over the sketches from Activity 14. If you wish to keep a record of your work it would be best to work on photocopies of your drawings (or you could use the overlay technique to copy them).

Convert your drawing of the two vertical cubes (Figure 76 stage 1) into two connected wedge shapes by simply drawing over the existing lines with your pen. Use the visible lines to assist you to put the lines of the wedges in the correct places (stage 2). Next place a sheet of layout paper over the image and redraw only the wedge shapes. Use shading to assist the illusion of three-dimensional form (stage 3).

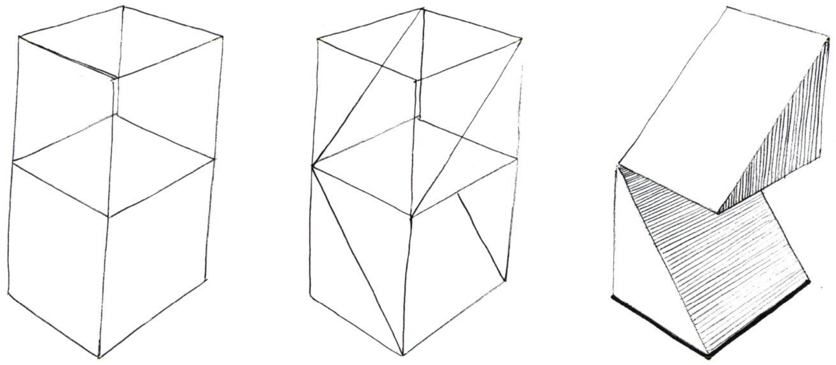

Stage 1 **Stage 2** **Stage 3**

Figure 76

If you want to take this further you can use this vertical double cube technique to design and present a number of abstract, geometric chess pieces. To increase the impact, add shading in your own preferred style but be consistent in your direction of light.

Next, convert your drawing of the two cubes side-by-side (or a photocopy of them) into a piece of imaginary furniture. Use the perspective lines that you already have to assist you to judge the new lines. Try to keep all vertical lines 'vertical'. You can either simply draw into the guide lines or use the tracing technique to create a more presentable image. Again, use your own preferred method of shading to increase the communication of 3D form. You can see a few of my ideas below but be adventurous in your own ideas!

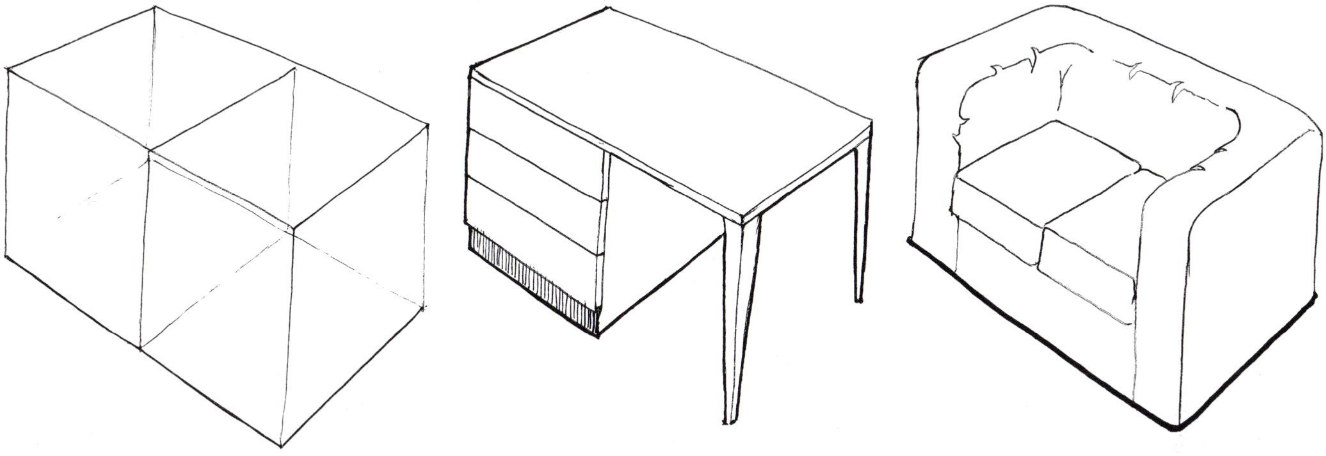

Figure 77 Furniture ideas developed from side-by-side double cube

Activity 15 demonstrates the value of using guide lines within which you can sketch more detailed information. The guide lines represent imaginary 'crates' that the products fit within. The perspective established for the crates guides our estimation of the perspective necessary in the subsequent sketch. It also assists in the estimation of proportions. It doesn't matter if our estimations are slightly out.

Using this type of drawing exploiting guide lines can provide a very accurate form of communication. Figures 78, 79 and 80 reveal how useful this 'crating' technique can be.

Examples of product sketching using the crating technique to establish guide lines

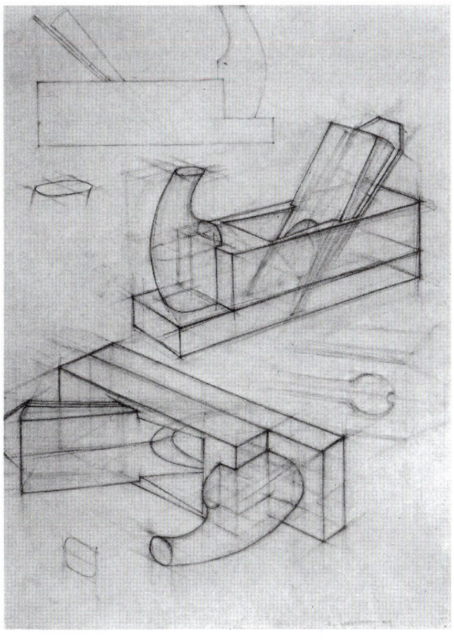

Figure 78 Plane

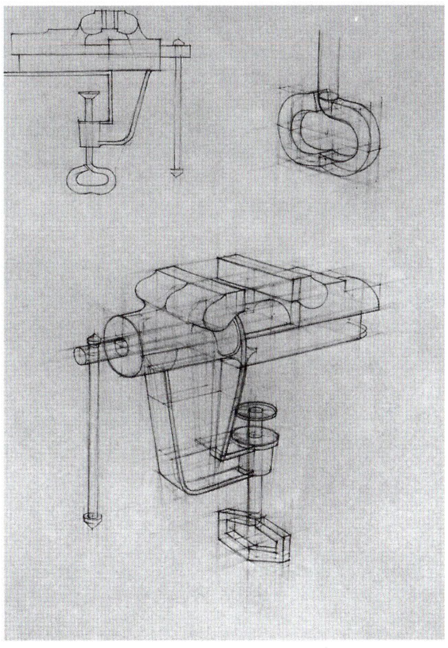

Figure 79 Clamp

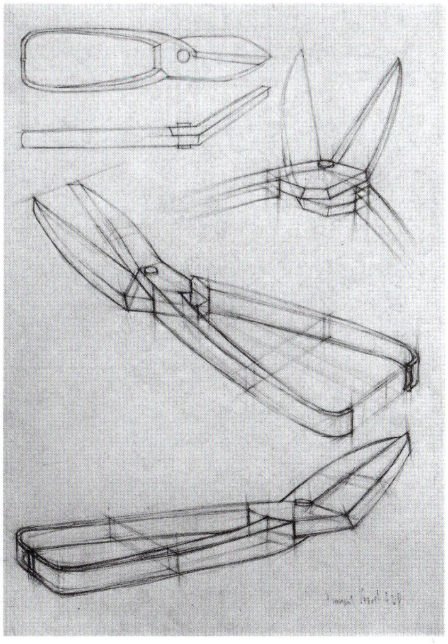

Figure 80 Shears

7 Perspective drawing 2

7.1 Circles and ovals

In Section 6 you made sketches of boxes. These 'crates' acted as guiding structures for more complex drawings but these had a common feature – they presented only flat-sided objects. In reality we find around us millions of different curved forms. We see curves in the cars we drive, the buildings we work in, and the products we own. Think of your local supermarket and the variety of curved forms available in, for example, the packaging of toiletries – shampoo bottles, toothpaste tubes and deodorants. If we are to use sketching to represent curved forms we need to look a little more closely at the basic elements. I'll start with a *circle*.

Figure 81 Curves around us – few products are made using only flat sides

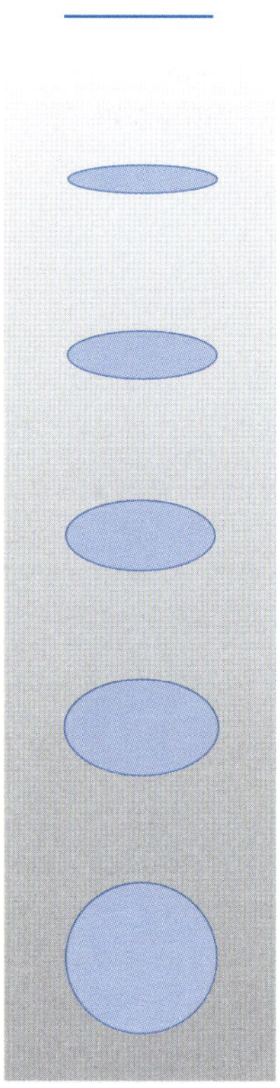

Figure 82

If you look at a circular object at an oblique angle it appears as a regular *oval*. Try looking at a CD, a plate or the top of a coffee mug. If you look straight down onto it, it appears circular; if you begin to tilt it you see the circle as an oval and if you bring it up at right angles to your eyes the circle becomes nothing more than a line (Figure 82).

These regular ovals have a number of qualities. They have major and minor axes about which they are symmetrical (Figure 83).

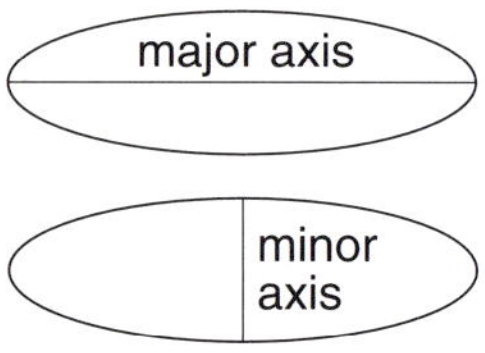

Figure 83

Just like circles, they don't have pointed ends. They have graceful, even curves. Let's draw some!

Activity 16 Sketching ovals

Toolkit

An A4 sheet of plain paper

A large sheet of scrap paper, e.g. from a roll of unwanted wallpaper

B or 2B pencil

Eraser

Ruler

1. Sketch freehand, a single horizontal line about 50 mm in length. This will become the major axis of a regular oval. In this first activity we will *not* draw-in a minor axis – just try to get your oval symmetrical about the major axis.
2. Resting you wrist on the table or on your drawing pad, and holding your pencil, move your pencil around the major axis line several times in an elliptical motion *but don't draw a line*. Just get the feel of the motion. This is a good general warm-up exercise to get your fingers prepared for all types of sketching activity.
3. When you feel comfortable and your pencil seems to be moving evenly around the line touch the pencil to the paper as you move. If you wish you can go around several times or you can try to achieve an oval in one pass.

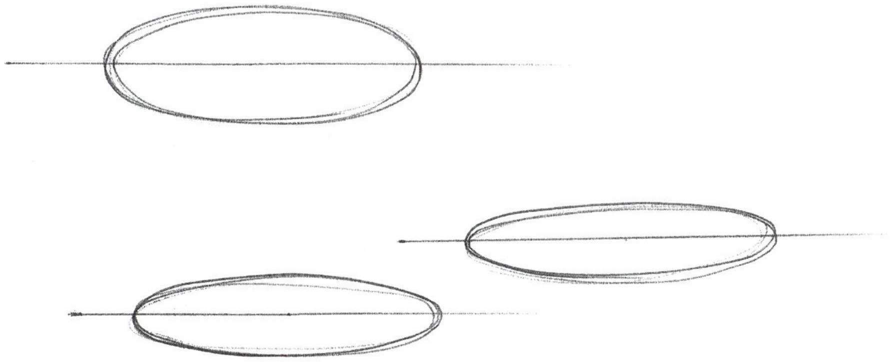

Figure 84

Repeat this several times. You might want to try some thick and some thin ovals (that is, varying the length of your imaginary minor axis). A good test of symmetry is to turn your paper upside down. Bulges and inaccuracies in regular ovals often seem much more apparent when viewed upside down!

When you feel comfortable working with just a major axis try adding a minor axis to predetermine the shape. Stick with a 50 mm major axis and try minor axes measuring 10 mm, 20 mm, and 40 mm. (The representations shown in Figure 85 may help guide your freehand versions).

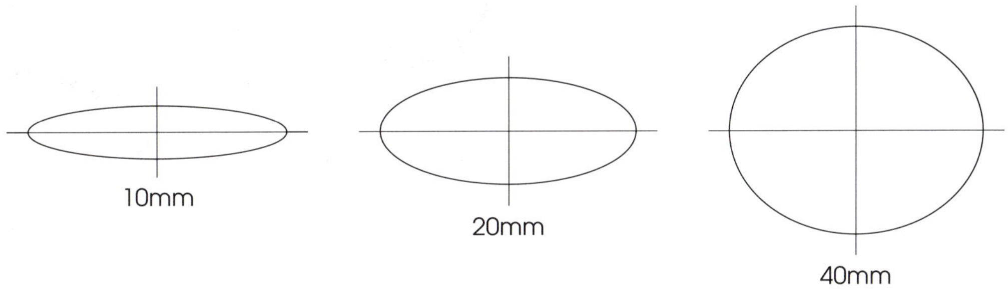

Figure 85

When you can achieve reasonable regular ovals with a 50 mm major axis try this activity using 100 mm, 200 mm and 300 mm major axes (you may define your own minor axes). Each of these larger ellipses will progressively require you to move your wrist, elbow and whole arm in creating accurate forms. Don't forget to warm up those limbs before drawing.

7.2 Cylinders and wheels

A drawing of a cylinder, such as a drinks can, is easily made using two ovals with their outer edges joined together (Figure 86).

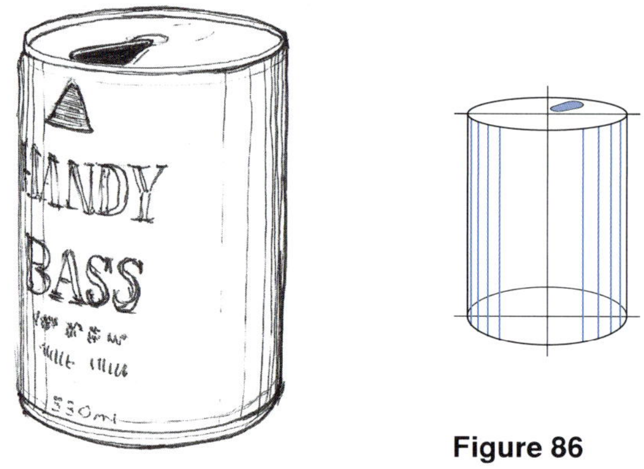

Figure 86

Let's look at the properties of this image.

The two ovals are almost the same size and shape. The two major axes are parallel with each other. Also their minor axes share a common line – it runs down the middle of the cylinder. These same features are found if we produce an image of a cylinder lying on its side (Figure 87).

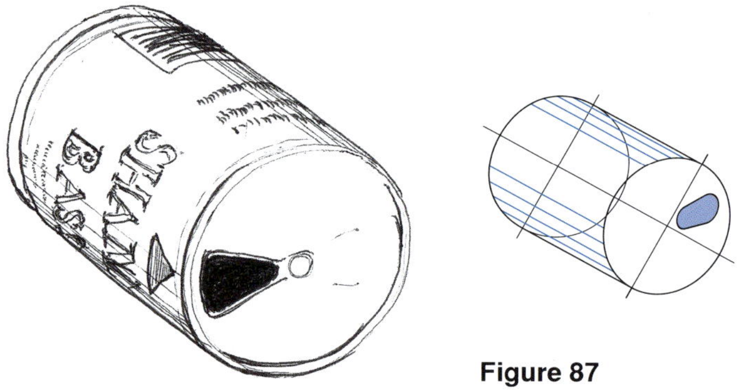

Figure 87

If we can determine the major and minor axes for any given regular oval then we can produce fairly realistic graphic representations of circles and cylinders as if they existed in three-dimensional space. It's a technique useful to sketching such things as wheels, arches, gears, cups, tins, bottles and buttons. We can combine this technique with the crating technique to provide us with a comprehensive network of guidelines for sketching products that possess cylindrical forms.

Figure 88 presents a cylinder and a box placed over their horizon lines. This gives the illusion that we, the viewers, are smaller than the object. In fact, I have tried to suggest two buildings here, both in an early stage of construction. We can see the framework and the floors before the walls are built. Notice how, in the cylinder, the size of the minor axes changes while the major axes remain the same. Also, see how the floors which lie exactly on the horizon line appear simply as a line – we see neither the upper or lower faces.

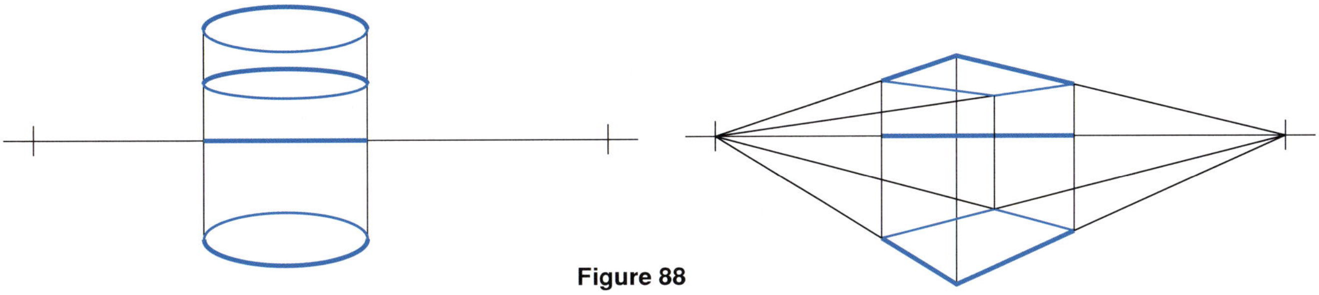

Figure 88

If I draw all the ovals identical in size it would indicate that perspective was not exercising its distorting effect. As we have seen in the sketch of the dice earlier the absence of this perspective distortion creates the impression of a small object. If the object is also drawn so that we, the viewer, see much of the top surface the illusion of a small object is enhanced.

Activity 17 Tins and bottles

Toolkit

An A3 sheet of plain paper
B or 2B pencil
Eraser
Ruler

Set up an arrangement of four cylindrical objects that you can find around your home or place of work. Cans, jars and cardboard rolls would be ideal. You can include bottles or other tapering cylinders if you are feeling adventurous because the principles of major and minor axes still hold true. Arrange some cylinders lying down and some standing up. Produce a pencil sketch of the collection on paper that is at least A3 in size.

My half-way point, shown in Figure 89, should help you set out your drawing. Figure 90 shows the finished sketch.

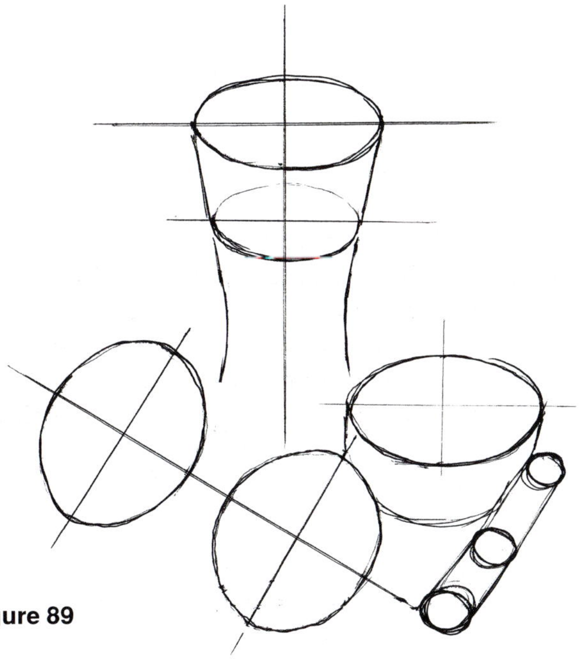

Figure 89

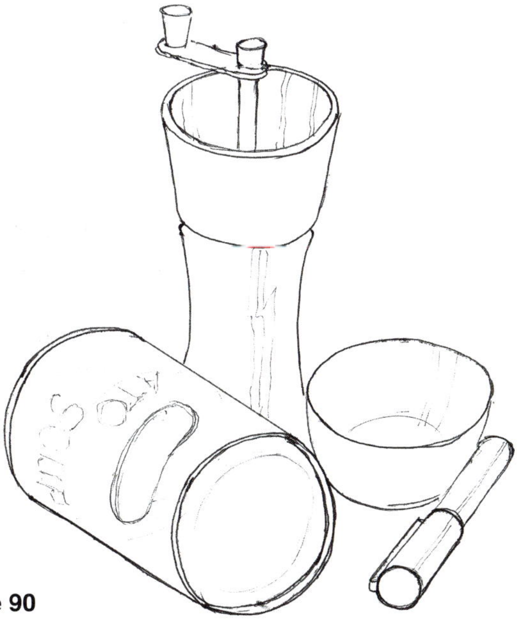

Figure 90

Figures 91 and 92 show some other examples of the technique used in Activity 17.

Figure 91

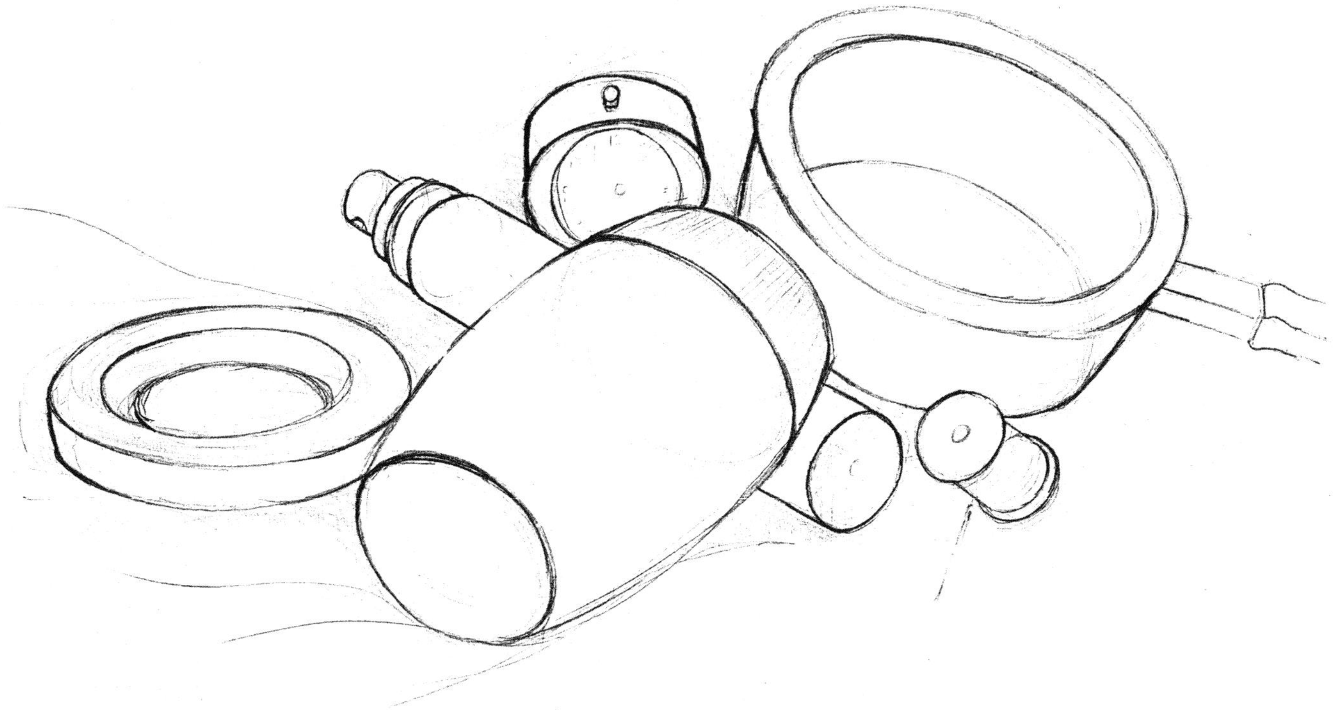

Figure 92

Activity 18 Sketching complex 3D products

Toolkit

Scrap paper

An A3 sheet of plain paper

Two A4 sheets of tracing paper

B or 2B pencil or any pen

Eraser

Ruler

This activity aims to combine the sketching of flat-sided forms with curved surfaces and cylinders. It will extend your skills with the crating technique introduced in Section 6.

I'd like you to use a child's toy as the subject for this activity. Perhaps the toy used in Activity 9. The components and the overall form need to be simple. It should have some flat surfaces, some curved surfaces and wheels or other cylinders. If you cannot use a toy select a small and basic household product or machine that has flat surfaces, some curved surfaces and a cylinder (e.g. coffee grinder, hand blender, electric drill). A photograph of my chosen object is shown in Figure 93.

Figure 93 Photo of toy tractor

1. Place the object in front of you and start by making a few small, rough 'thumbnail' perspective sketches on scrap paper. These are intended to help you to work out your preferred orientation for the crate and how dramatic to make the perspective.
2. When you've got a crate that seems suitable, recreate it on an A3 sheet of paper but this time much bigger. There is no need to define precise vanishing points for this crate. Just make an estimate.
3. Build up guide lines inside this crate to define where the basic components of your object will go. Try to define the main volumes and proportions but don't add any detail yet. These guide lines will include the central axis of any cylinders or wheels in your object.
4. When you are happy that the basic proportions are correct you can start to add outlines and details. Use the crate guide lines to assist you to keep the perspective consistent.
5. Where you are drawing ovals to represent wheels or the tops of cylinders take care to place your major axis at right angles to the axis of the cylinder. You will need to estimate the appropriate lengths of your minor and major axes.
6. Use the tracing paper to copy your final drawing and recreate it on a new A3 sheet of paper. (To do this, once you have copied the image, turn the tracing paper over onto the plain paper and redraw the lines to transfer a 'reversed' image.) Alternatively, use the overlay technique.

My sequence of stages is shown below.

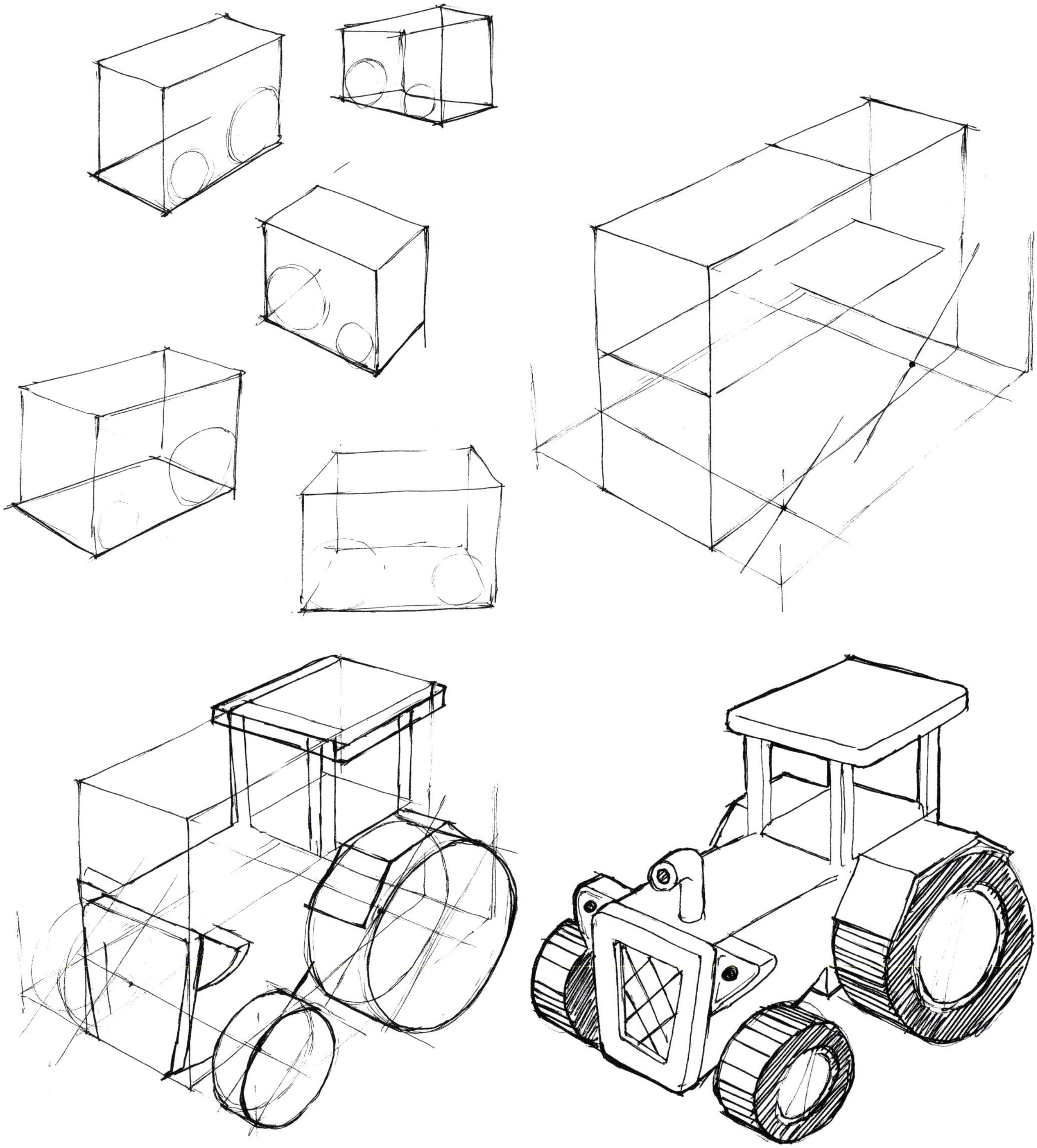

Figure 94 Sequence of sketches for drawing the toy tractor

7.3 Shading on cylindrical forms

The shading activities presented in Section 2 used only objects with flat sides. In these the cross-hatching and tone were applied evenly and there was strong contrast between surfaces. Cylinders and other curved surfaces, on the other hand, are usually characterised by smooth transitions in tone. Shading must be *graded* from light to dark – from no tone to deep tone.

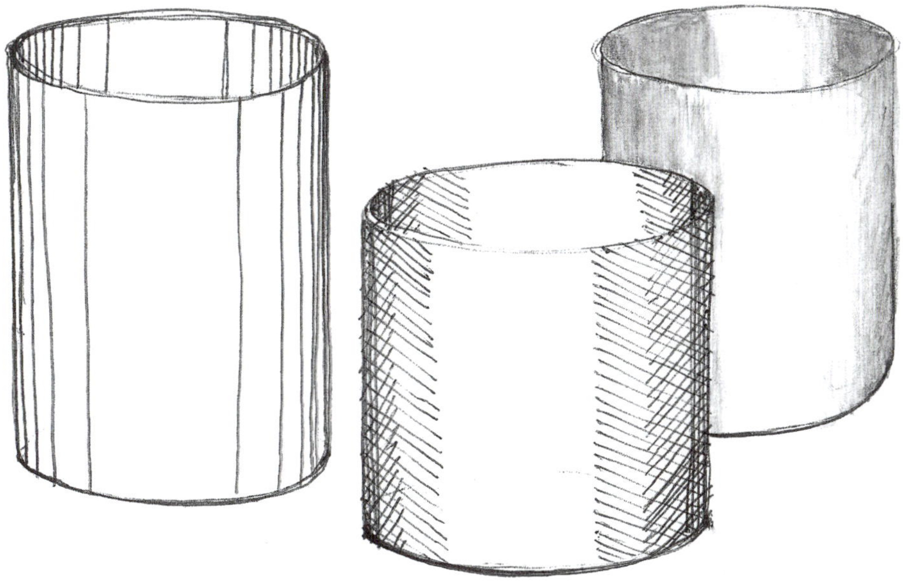

Figure 95 Styles of shading for cylindrical forms

You use all the same styles of shading – cross-hatching, textures or tone – but the techniques of applying them must be altered. Some techniques are fast and seek to provide only a crude indication of this grading. Other techniques are time-consuming but produce a more even grading in the tone. The former are probably more use in sketching while the latter are seen in drawings where precise communication of surface quality is intended.

The shading may be applied using lines in any direction but vertical or sloping lines are most usual. A gradation of tone can be achieved by selectively layering one set of lines over another, the most worked sections located where you wish the deepest shade to be (the opposite side to your source of light).

7.4 Assemblies of components

Most of the products we find around us are not made from one single piece of material – they are made from an assembly of separate components. Very complex products such as a motor car may have thousands of components made from numerous different materials. As well as being put together as part of their manufacture these components may be designed to come apart, for example taking the top off a container or taking a garden chair apart to store it away. A lot of design sketching is used to convey the relationship of component parts to each other and to the overall product.

Figure 96(b) to (d) show drawings of a soap dispenser with a lift-off top. There are two points to note here:

1 in each sketch all the component parts are drawn using the same estimated vanishing points (this makes them seem part of the same drawing);

2 the arrows assist us to understand how components move (the lid lifting vertically upwards and the dispenser unscrewing). Figure 96(a) shows my first rough sketch. I used this and the overlay technique to create the other sketches.

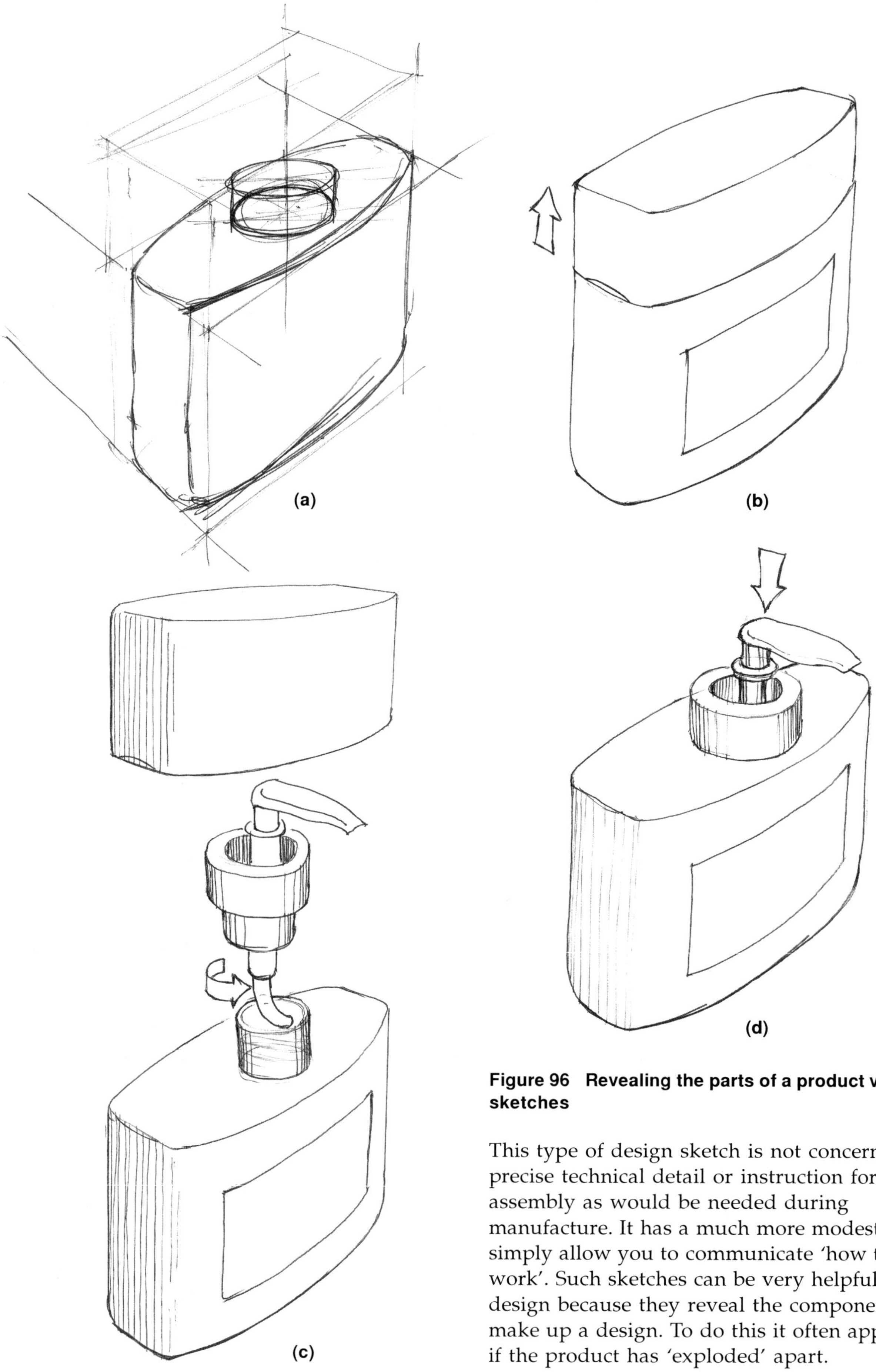

Figure 96 Revealing the parts of a product via sketches

This type of design sketch is not concerned with precise technical detail or instruction for assembly as would be needed during manufacture. It has a much more modest aim – to simply allow you to communicate 'how things work'. Such sketches can be very helpful in design because they reveal the components that make up a design. To do this it often appears as if the product has 'exploded' apart.

You may have spotted a similarity between the type of sketch used to communicate the components of the soap dispenser and the type of drawing often included with self-assembly furniture or those sketches that appear in manuals showing how to replace batteries or an ink cartridge in a printer. Often these drawings are very precisely drawn because of the number of components and the complexity of the sequence of actions but the purpose is the same – drawings are being used to show 'how things work'. The next activity involves you in making sketches that show how things work.

Activity 19 Sketching 'how things work'

Toolkit

An A4 sheet of plain paper

Scrap paper

B or 2B pencil or any pen

Pencil eraser (if necessary)

This activity is about making a sequence of sketches that communicate a simple process. Look at my examples below in Figure 97.

The first shows a frozen pizza being removed from its cardboard packaging, then having its cellophane wrapper removed and then being put in the oven. Note the use of perspective sketches and arrows.

(a) Cooking a pizza

(b) Sticking a self-adhesive stamp on an envelope and posting the letter

Figure 97

Your task is to select a simple activity and to use sketching to convey the sequence of actions necessary to complete the activity. Imagine you are trying to communicate this activity to another person so they could carry out the sequence of actions.

Using either a pencil or any pen try to cover your entire sequence by making between three and five sketches on one sheet of plain A4 paper (you might find it helpful to roughly sketch out your ideas first on scrap paper).

Make your communication as clear as possible. You may need to construct simple crates to assist you in this. Use arrows *but no words* in your communication of actions. You might like to try giving your sequence of actions to somebody else and see if they can understand them or carry them out successfully.

Activity 20 Product analysis with sketches

Toolkit

A4 sheet of plain paper

A4 sheet of squared paper

B or 2B pencil or any pen

Pencil eraser (if necessary)

tracing paper

This final activity brings together many of the skills and techniques you have developed as you worked through this book. It aims to get you using drawing as a normal part of analysing and communicating your own product ideas. It provides some useful practice in preparation for the course project (TMA 06).

Select a product that you have easy access to. It might be, for example, a kitchen gadget, an item of furniture or a toy.

Caution. If you choose an electrical product do not plug it in or remove any protective covers. Your analysis concerns only the external form and the usability of the product in a normal situation.

There are four parts to this activity and I have illustrated each with reference to my choice of product – a vacuum cleaner.

1. Measure the main dimensions of your product and draw a sketch of two orthographic views to a suitable scale on squared paper (I have selected the front elevation and the side elevation for my cleaner and drawn them at a scale of 1:10; see Figure 98)
2. With the product in front of you for reference, make a perspective sketch on plain paper. You will probably need to lightly construct a perspective crate, subdivided in order to get the proportions of the product correct (Figure 99).
3. Select any moveable feature of this product and make some sketches that communicate this feature to a person who has not used this product before (as I did for the soap dispenser earlier). I have chosen to show how by removing the front cover the waste bag can be accessed (Figure 100).
4. Use sketches to suggest one design improvement to your selected product. In mine, I have focused on the handle because I find it uncomfortable. I made perspective sketches on plain paper of the old version and used the overlay technique (with tracing paper) to help me generate new sketches for a more comfortable handle (Figure 101).

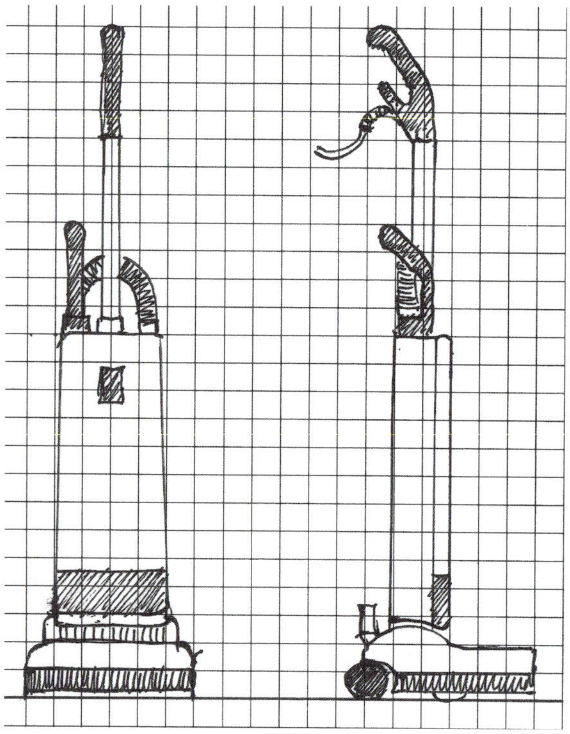

Figure 98

Figure 99

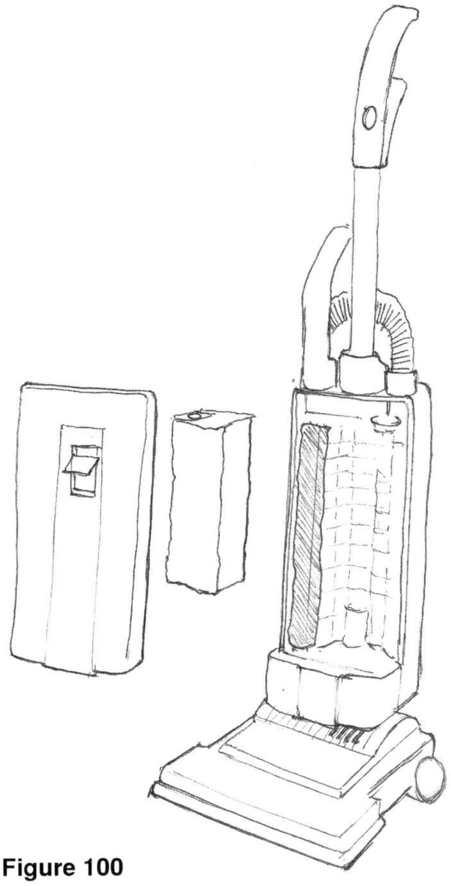

Figure 100

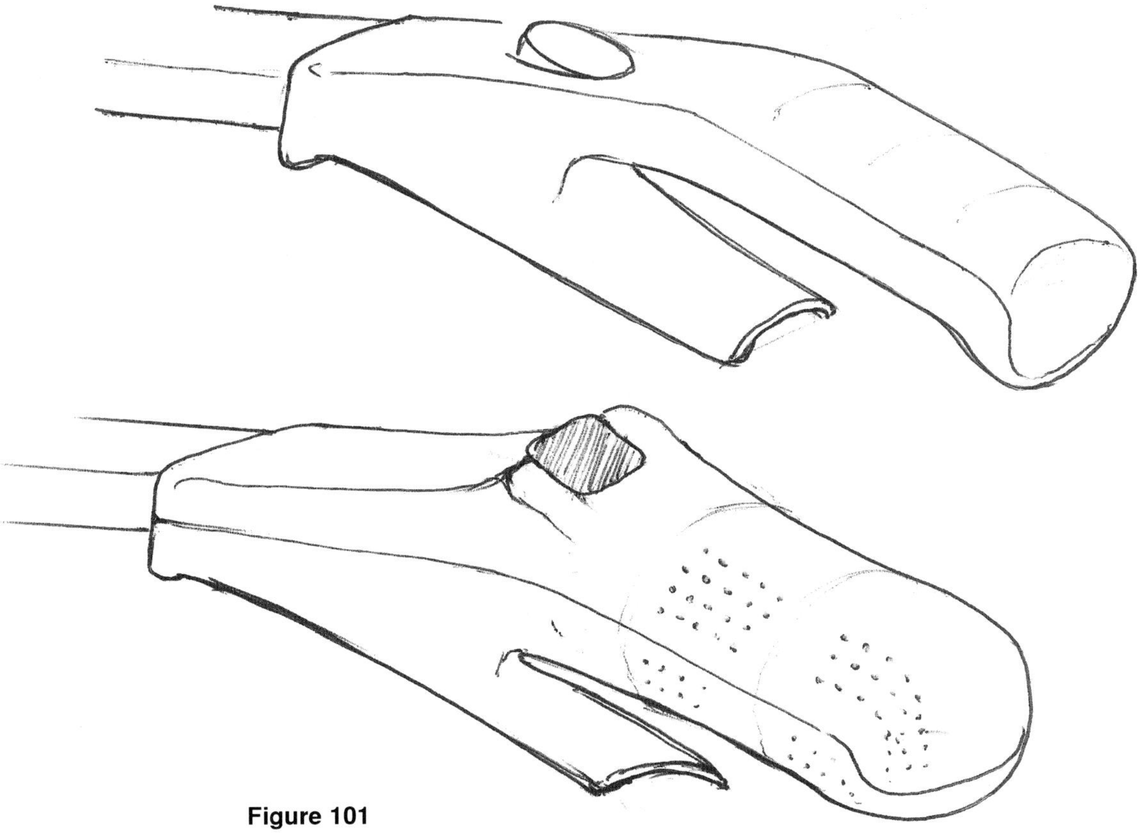

Figure 101

Section 8 Summary

Design modelling can be a very powerful tool and drawing can be particularly effective. Drawing can help us inspect objects, we can learn about manufacture, components and the way designs do and don't work for people. Drawing can heighten our awareness of visual qualities in design such as shape, texture and colour. Drawing can allow us to share what we've noticed and learned. The more you examine and draw objects the more you will become aware of the qualities of good design.

Also visualising what does exist, can help us to put on paper new ideas taking shape in our minds. Drawing can help us be more creative. We can explore ideas and develop them. As well as *'looking* and drawing' we can use *'thinking* and drawing'. But of course all these demand practise if you are to use sketching effectively in your TMAs and in the examination at the end of the course. Freehand sketching is your best and most liberating design tool.

Consider the following points that summarise some of the drawing advice presented throughout this workbook.

Viewpoint

From which direction and from what height do you want to show an object? What angle will best display its features? The presentation and orientation of an object can influence the way viewers read your drawing.

Perspective

Even when you are estimating your vanishing points be aware that they lie on a single 'horizon' line. Your drawing will look more realistic if your lines are consistent with your vanishing points.

Proportion and profile

Lightly draw a box or 'crate' to assist you when sketching complex objects. Crates help you define the proportions of an object, they provide reference points and they help maintain consistency with vanishing points. Get the profiles of a shape correct on the paper before spending time sketching any details.

Line quality

All pens and pencils make different marks. Experiment so that you know what's possible. Aim to control each media. Be conscious of your finger, hand and arm movement. Make quick 'warm-up' drawings if necessary. Develop your own style but make sure your sketches communicate what you intend.

Shadow and shading

These can improve the illusion of three-dimensionality in drawings. It's important to be consistent, e.g. all upper surfaces presented in the lightest tones. When drawing objects with flat surfaces crosshatching or tone is applied evenly to each surface. When drawing cylinders and other curved surfaces the shading needs to be graded from light to dark.

Answers to self-assessment questions

SAQ 1

There is no model answer given to SAQ 1.

SAQ 2

Full-size rough 3D models such as the Dyson vacuum cleaner model in card are very useful in design. How might this rough Dyson model be used to assist design activity?

I can suggest a number of possible uses:

- the models assist the designers to better understand their own thinking. They give a tangible form to ideas;
- designers might show their models to others and ask for opinions on shape, size, or their general impressions. Negative opinions could be especially welcome if they enabled a better definition of the problem or the development of product features;
- the model might be used to undertake some basic user trials. For example, a selection of potential users might be asked to go through the motions of using it or interacting with it. This might provide some feedback about the user interface;
- the card models might be shown to retailers or manufacturers in order to get feedback on, for example, comparisons, marketing, decoration or packaging.

In each case the feedback received might allow the designers to revise the concept before a great deal of time has been spent developing a particular idea.

Acknowledgments

Grateful acknowledgement is made to the following sources for permission to reproduce material within this book:

Photos/illustrations

Figure 2: © Mark Evans, Figures 17 right, 19, 24, 26, 27, 40c and 91: Student designers unknown, Loughborough University; Figure 17 left: Jon Sutton, Loughborough University; Figure 17 centre: Norman Edwards, Loughborough University; Figure 34: Dyson Ltd; Figure 37: © British Motor Industry Heritage Trust; Figure 40(b) and 44: Sketches by Paul O' Leary; Figure 57 and 58: Sketches by Andy Rogers; Figures 78-80: Manfred Maier, Basic Principles of Design, Vol. 1, Van Nostrand/Reinhold, (1977) Figure 92: Mark Redgrave, Loughborough University.

Every effort has been made to contact copyright owners. If any have been overlooked, the publishers will be happy to make the necessary arrangements at the first opportunity.

Course Team

Academic staff

Ken Baynes, External Assessor
Catherine Cooke, Author
Nigel Cross, Author
Chris Earl, Author
Steve Garner, Author and Course Chair
Georgy Holden, Author
Robin Roy, Author

Consultants

Mark Evans, Contributing Author, Workbook 1

Associate lecturers

Jenny Burke
Nick Jeffrey

Course managers

Andy Harding, Course Manager
Amber Thomas, Course Manager

Production staff

Tammy Alexander, Graphic Designer
Margaret Barnes, Course Secretary
Philippa Broadbent, Print Buyer
Jane Bromley, Interactive Media Designer
Michael Brown, Video Editor
Daphne Cross, Assistant Print Buyer
Tony Duggan, Learning Projects Manager
Bernie D'Souza, Course Secretary
Barbara Fraser, Picture Researcher
Phil Gauron, Video Producer
Richard Hearne, Photographer
Katie Meade, Rights Executive
Jane Moore, Editor
Jonathon Owen, Graphic Artist
Alex Reid, Narrator (video)
Ekkehard Thumm, Media Project Manager
Howie Twiner, Graphic Artist
Robert Wood, Editor